Launching on Inland Waterways

A new guide to launching sites on
Britain's canals and rivers

Compiled by
Diana van der Klugt

ERRATUM

 Page 18 The telephone number for *Willowtree
Marina* should read Tel: 081-841-6585

Acknowledgements

I would like to thank Ron T. Martin of the CaraCruiser Club for invaluable assistance and advice given during the early stages of preparation of the book and Wendy Robinson for considerable editorial assistance.

Design and production: Julia Gray

Printed by: ESP, Crowborough, East Sussex

Photography:
Front cover: Colin Wilson
Back cover: Colin Graham, Wilderness boats

First edition 1993

ISBN 1 898574 00 6

Contents

Introduction

Launching on Inland Waterways is designed to serve as a guide to the location and availability of 275 selected launching sites on the navigable rivers and canals of Great Britain. It is intended to be useful to owners of all types of boats, from those launching small dinghies near home to those who regularly trail their boats in search of new cruising grounds, as well as the narrowboat owner wishing to move or launch a boat. This book is not a guide to the waterways themselves as there are already a number of excellent books and maps on the market which can be purchased from any good nautical bookshop or chandler.

The waterways included in this guide are listed alphabetically with a comprehensive index enabling the user to easily select sites. Each waterway is headed by a brief historic description followed by the name and address of the British Waterways area manager, National River Authority or other body, which is in charge of the waterway.

Each site entry is headed by the name, address and phone number of the owner followed by concise site details. These include: size of craft that can be accommodated; the times when the site is available; restrictions as to its use, such as difficult or narrow access and locked gates; facilities available at or near the site i.e. fuel, water, parking [(c) indicates a charge], moorings and repairs; licensing authority (see next page); whether or not a charge is made and finally brief directions to the site and linking waterways.

Before visiting any site it is recommended that you contact the owner to ascertain its suitability for your particular needs and it should be appreciated that during busy summer weekends many boatyards and marinas are not able to accommodate casual launching.

While the information in this guide was correct at the time of going to press, changes in yard ownership are frequent and waterway restoration projects are progressing all the time. If you find something has changed or you know of a site that you feel should be included, please let us know. That way we can ensure that our next guide is as up-to-date and as helpful as possible.

Before Setting Out

Licences

In the majority of cases, the boat owner is required to obtain a licence before launching a boat. The address and telephone number of the licensing authority for each waterway is given at the head of each section and should be contacted directly.

All British Waterway licences can be obtained from the following address:

Customer Services,
British Waterways,
Greycaine Road,
Watford WD2 4JR

Telephone (0923) 226422

Site charges

Site charges will be levied by the owner in the majority of cases. Details of specific charges have not been given as they vary greatly depending on the size of craft, type of launch and other factors. Contact the individual site owners for details.

Dimensions

This guide lists sites on both broad and narrow canals; before choosing your launching site be sure to ascertain the craft dimensions which a particular waterway can accommodate.

AIRE AND CALDER CANAL   BW (North East Region)

Mike Harrison, Lock Lane, Castleford, West Yorks WF1O 2LH
Tel: (0977) 554351

Improvements to the River Aire were first made in 1700, enabling coal to be taken. from the Yorkshire coalfields and agricultural produce to be brought in. The canal still carries a significant volume of commercial traffic.

Smith Bros (Goole) Ltd Marina, Goole, Humberside
Tel: (0405) 763985

Suits:	craft up to 36' LOA and 11'6" wide
Availability:	during working hours or by prior arrangement if assistance required
Restrictions:	check for availability
Facilities:	diesel, parking for car and trailer(c), toilets, boatyard with boat lift
Licence:	BW licence
Charge:	yes
Directions:	follow M62 east from M18 to Goole then signs to the Sobriety Centre which is adjacent to site
Link:	River Ouse, Humber Estuary and North Sea, Calder and Hebble and Leeds and Liverpool Canals

Stanley Ferry Marina, Ferry Lane, Stanley Ferry, Wakefield, West Yorks
Tel: (0924) 290596

Suits:	all craft
Availability:	0900-2100 in summer: 0900-1800 in winter
Restrictions:	none
Facilities:	diesel, parking for car and trailer(c), sewage and refuse disposal, water, gas, pump-out, toilets and showers, overnight moorings, chandlery, pub
Licence:	BW licence
Charge:	yes
Directions:	follow the A642 north east from Wakefield, turning off into Ferry Lane
Link:	River Ouse, Humber Estuary and North Sea, Calder and Hebble and Leeds and Liverpool Canals

RIVER ANCHOLME   NRA (Anglian Region)

Kingfisher House, Goldhay Way, Orton Goldhay, Peterborough PE2 OZR
Tel: (0733) 371811

The river is navigable for approximately 25 miles from the entrance from the River Humber at South Ferriby to Harlem Hill Lock at Snitterby. There is a speed limit of 7mph from South Ferriby to Brigg, and 4mph on the rest of the river. Before entering the river, inform the lock-keeper at South Ferriby Tel: (0652) 635219: the lock is manned 24 hours a day from 1st april - 30th october.

Clapson Marina, Red Lane, South Ferriby, Barton on Humber, Humberside
Tel: (0652) 635620

Suits:	all craft
Availability:	during working hours by arrangement.
Restrictions:	launching by crane only
Facilities:	fuel, parking for car and trailer(c), toilets, chandlery
Licence:	NRA licence
Charge:	yes
Directions:	turn off A1077 Scunthorpe to Barton Road at South Ferriby Sluice
Link:	access also to tidal River Humber via sluice lock

RIVER ARUN

Littlehampton Harbour Board, Harbour Office, Pier Road, Littlehampton, West Sussex
Tel: (0903) 721215

Tides run strongly in the lower reaches of the river which is tidal to Pallingham. There is a speed limit of 6 knots from Littlehampton to Arundel Bridge and 5.5 knots above Arundel Bridge.

Littlehampton Marina, Ferry Road, Littlehampton, West Sussex
Tel: (0903) 713553

Suits:	all craft
Availability:	from HW-4 to HW+5 by prior arrangement
Restrictions:	launching by yard staff only: insurance certificate required for craft
Facilities:	fuel, parking for car and trailer, toilets and showers, chandlery, boat-yard with crane, diving
Licence:	harbour dues payable
Charge:	yes
Directions:	follow the A284/259 from Arundel, crossing the river and turning left after half a mile: site is on west bank downstream of bridge
Link:	access to open sea one mile downstream

Fisherman's Quay, Surrey Street, Littlehampton, West Sussex
Tel: (0903) 721215

Suits:	small craft
Availability:	daylight hours - best near HW
Restrictions:	steep slipway (1:6) into soft mud may require 4-wheel drive vehicle
Facilities:	fuel from local garage, parking for car and trailer under 14' long
Licence:	harbour dues payable
Charge:	small fee may be payable
Directions:	follow the A284 from Arundel and signs to town centre
Link:	access to open sea

Ship and Anchor Marina, Ford, Nr. Arundel, West Sussex
Tel: (0243) 551262

Suits:	small craft
Availability:	for approx. 4 hours either side HW only
Restrictions:	launching by yard staff only using tractor at owner's risk
Facilities:	no fuel, parking for car and trailer, telephone, toilet
Licence:	harbour dues payable
Charge:	yes
Directions:	from the A27 at Arundel take the Ford road: site is after the station
Link:	access to open sea

Swan Corner, Pulborough, West Sussex

Suits:	craft up to 15' LOA
Availability:	launch near HW
Restrictions:	slipway is steep with snatch block requiring at least 40m rope: access is difficult
Facilities:	limited parking here or at station(c) nearby, toilets in village, Swan Inn
Licence:	no
Charge:	no
Directions:	turn off the A29 Bognor road at junction with A283: site is adjacent east side of bridge on north bank
Link:	access to open sea

ASHBY CANAL   (BW Midlands Region)

Roger Herrington, Maintenance Yard, Atherstone Road, Hartshill, Nuneaton, Warks CV10 0TB
Tel: (0203) 392250

Originally planned to connect the Coventry Canal to the River Trent, the canal was actually only built as far as Moira, but prospered transporting high quality coal from the Ashby Coalfields to southern England. Some of the canal has now been abandoned but it is navigable for nearly 22 miles to Snarestone: there are no locks.

Ashby Narrowboat Co, The Canal Wharf, Stoke Golding, Nuneaton, Leics
Tel: (0455) 212671

Suits:	canoes and dinghies only
Availability:	during daylight hours
Restrictions:	no slipway: launching from wharf
Facilities:	diesel, sewage and refuse disposal, water, gas, pump-out, toilets, overnight moorings, boatyard, engine repairs, shop and cream teas
Licence:	BW licence
Charge:	yes
Directions:	stay on the A5, turning off at the roundabout to Stoke Golding
Link:	Coventry Canal at Marston Junction

Canal Terminus, Snarestone, Leics

Ashby Canal Assoc. 9 St. Catherine's Avenue, Market Bosworth, Nuneaton, Warks
Tel: (0455) 290129

Suits:	all craft
Availability:	by prior arrangement only
Restrictions:	for use of members only
Facilities:	rubbish and sewage disposal and water at bridge 61 nearby
Licence:	BW licence
Charge:	yes
Directions:	turn off A5 north of Nuneaton onto A444, then turn onto B4116
Link:	Coventry Canal at Marston Junction

RIVER AVON (BRISTOL)   BW (South West Region)

Brian Rodgers, Regional Manager, Llanthony Warehouse, Gloucester Docks,
Gloucester GL1 2EH
Tel: (0452) 525524

The canalised river is tidal as far as Hanham Lock and is controlled by the Port of
Bristol Authority. Between Hanham and Bath it is controlled by BW with whom any
boat using this stretch of the river should be registered. There is no public right of
navigation above Pulteney Weir in Bath and there is a speed limit of 4 mph on the
river. The Kennet and Avon Canal joins the river in Bath, immediately after Bath
Lower lock.

Bath Marina, Brassmill Lane, Bath, (Bath and Newbridge Marine Services Ltd).
Tel: (0225) 424301

Suits:	dinghies, trailer-sailers and river boats
Availability:	0900-1730 daily by appointment only
Restrictions:	none
Facilities:	diesel, parking for car and trailer(c), sewage and refuse disposal, water, pump-out, toilets, overnight moorings, chandlery, yard facilities including crane if required(c), pub and restaurant
Licence:	BW licence and boat insurance required
Charge:	yes
Directions:	turn off A4 two miles west of Bath city centre at Newbridge
Link:	Kennet and Avon Canal, Bristol Channel and River Severn

Saltford Marina, The Shallows, Saltford, Nr. Bristol, Avon
Tel: (0225) 872226

Suits:	craft up to 27' LOA with draught less than 0.9m
Availability:	during daylight hours
Restrictions:	none
Facilities:	diesel, petrol (10 mins walk), parking for car and trailer, refuse disposal, water, toilets and showers, overnight moorings, chandlery, boatyard, crane by arrangement, bar and restaurant
Licence:	BW licence

Charge: yes
Directions: access is from the A4 Bristol to Bath road turning into The Shallows (Bath end). It is best to head into The Shallows from Bath due to a very tight left hand turn encountered if coming from Bristol
Link: Kennet and Avon Canal, Bristol Channel and River Severn

Bristol Boats, by Saltford Lock, Mead Lane, Saltford, Nr Bristol, Avon
Tel: (0225) 872032

Suits:	craft up to 20' LOA
Availability:	daily 1000 - 1730 in summer but closed sun in winter
Restrictions:	none
Facilities:	gas, chandlery, boatyard, engine repairs
Licence:	BW licence
Charge:	yes
Directions:	follow the A4 Bath to Bristol road turning off to Saltford Lock
Link:	Kennet and Avon Canal, Bristol Channel and River Severn

Portavon Marine, Bitton Road, Keynsham, Avon
Tel: (0272) 861626

Suits:	all craft
Availability:	0900-1700 daily
Restrictions:	boats over 19' LOA must have assisted slip(c)
Facilities:	diesel, petrol (.5 mile), parking for car and trailer, sewage and refuse disposal, water, gas, toilets and showers, overnight moorings, chandlery and boatyard with crane and winch, engine repairs
Licence:	BW licence
Charge:	yes
Directions:	leave A4 at Keynsham and follow A4175 over bridge
Link:	Kennet and Avon Canal, Bristol Channel and River Severn

Jondeblin Marine, Broadmead Lane, Keynsham, Nr. Bristol, Avon
Tel: (0272) 861168

Suits:	all craft
Availability:	by prior arrangement only
Restrictions:	launching by 60 ton crane only
Facilities:	diesel, parking for car and trailer(c), sewage and refuse disposal, water, pump-out, toilets, overnight moorings, chandlery, boatyard
Licence:	BW licence
Charge:	yes
Directions:	turn off A4 at Keynsham west of Bath
Link:	Kennet and Avon Canal, Bristol Channel and River Severn

Chequers Inn, Hanham, Bristol, Avon
Tel: (0272) 674242

Suits:	craft up to 23' LOA
Availability:	by arrangement during daylight hours
Restrictions:	steep slipway
Facilities:	fuel, parking for car and trailer, refuse disposal, water, toilets, overnight moorings
Licence:	BW licence
Charge:	yes
Directions:	turn off A431 at Hanham and follow minor roads to lock
Link:	Kennet and Avon Canal, Bristol Channel and River Severn

RIVER AVON (WARWICKSHIRE)

Evesham Lock to Alveston Sluice - Upper Avon Navigation Trust, Avon House, Harvington, Evesham, Worcs Tel: (0386) 870526

Evesham Lock to Tewkesbury - Lower Avon Navigation Trust, Mill Wharf, Mill Lane, Wyre Piddle, Pershore, Worcs WR10 2JF Tel: (0386) 552517

The river is navigable for just over 45 miles from Alveston Sluice, north of Stratford-on-Avon, to its junction with the River Severn a short distance below Mythe Bridge in Tewkesbury. There is a speed limit of 6mph on the Lower Avon and 4mph on the Upper Avon.

Stratford Marina, Clopton Bridge, Stratford-on-Avon, Warks
Tel: (0789) 269669

Suits:	craft up to 27' LOA.
Availability:	mar-oct 0830-1830 daily, nov-feb 0830-1600 mon-sat
Restrictions:	none
Facilities:	fuel, parking for car and trailer(c), sewage and refuse disposal, water, gas, pump-out, overnight moorings, chandlery and boatyard
Licence:	Upper Avon - obtainable from site
Charge:	yes
Directions:	access is from the A3400 gyratory one-way system in the town centre via signposted driveway adjacent to the Moat House International Hotel by Clopton Bridge
Link:	River Severn and Bristol Channel, Stratford-on-Avon Canal

Bidford Boats, 4 The Pleck, Bidford-on-Avon, Warks
Tel: (0789) 773205

Suits:	craft up to 25' LOA
Availability:	0900-1800 daily in summer
Restrictions:	none

Facilities:	petrol from garage nearby, parking for car and trailer(c), sewage disposal, water, pump out, overnight moorings
Licence:	Upper Avon available on site
Charge:	yes
Directions:	follow A439 west from Stratford-upon-Avon to Bidford-on-Avon: entrance is opposite the Reliance Garage
Link:	River Severn and Bristol Channel, Stratford-on-Avon Canal

Barton Cruisers, Welford Road, Barton, Warks
Tel: (0789) 772003

Suits:	all craft
Availability:	0900-1800 daily in summer
Restrictions:	none
Facilities:	fuel (1 mile), parking for car and trailer(c), limited chandlery
Licence:	Upper Avon
Charge:	yes
Directions:	follow A439 west from Stratford-on-Avon turning left over the river at Bidford-on-Avon onto the B4085 Honeybourne Road; take first left turning to Barton and site is on left
Link:	River Severn and Bristol Channel, Stratford-on-Avon Canal

Evesham Marina, King's Road, Evesham, Worcs
Tel: (0386) 47813

Suits:	all shallow-draught craft
Availability:	0900-1700 daily
Restrictions:	steep slipway
Facilities:	fuel, parking for car and trailer(c), refuse disposal, water, gas, pump-out, toilets, overnight moorings, boatyard, engine repairs
Licence:	Upper Avon
Charge:	yes
Directions:	leave M5 at junction 7 following A44 east to Evesham
Link:	River Severn and Bristol Channel, Statford-on-Avon Canal

Sankey Marine, Worcester Road, Evesham, Worcs
Tel: (0386) 442338

Suits:	all craft
Availability:	0800-1800 in summer
Restrictions:	none
Facilities:	fuel, parking for car and trailer(c), water, gas, toilets and showers, overnight moorings, chandlery and yard facilities, engine repairs
Licence:	Lower Avon
Charge:	yes
Directions:	leave M5 at junction 7 following the A44 east to Pershore, turning onto the B4083/B4084: site is below the Abbey Manor House
Link:	River Severn and Bristol Channel, Stratford-on-Avon Canal

Sanders Boatyard, Pensham Road, Pershore, Worcs

Tel: (0386) 552765

Suits:	all craft up to 30' LOA
Availability:	0900-1300 and 1400-1800 daily
Restrictions:	steep slipway
Facilities:	fuel, parking for car and trailer(c), toilets, chandlery and boatyard
Licence:	Lower Avon
Charge:	yes
Directions:	follow M5, turning off at junction 7 onto A44: at Pershore new bridge turn right then fork right and the entrance drive is on the right
Link:	River Severn and Bristol Channel, Stratford-on-Avon Canal

Tewkesbury Marina, Bredon Road, Tewkesbury, Glos

Tel: (0684) 293737

Suits:	all craft
Availability:	during weekday working hours by arrangement
Restrictions:	no slipway: launching by hoist only
Facilities:	fuel, trailers can be left(c), sewage and refuse disposal, water, gas, pump-out, overnight moorings, chandlery and boatyard, engine repairs
Licence:	Lower Avon
Charge:	yes
Directions:	leave M5 at junction 9, taking A438 then A38 and B4080
Link:	River Severn and Bristol Channel

BASINGSTOKE CANAL   Basingstoke Canal Authority

Basingstoke Canal Office, Ash Lock Depot, Government Road, Aldershot, Hants GU11 2PS
Tel: (0252) 313810

The canal is now navigable from Woodham Junction, where it joins the River Wey, for nearly 31 miles to the limit of navigation just before Greywell Tunnel. Before launching, a licence should be obtained from the canal office. There is a speed limit of 4mph on the canal.

Potters Pub Slipway, Mytchett Place Road, Mytchett, Surrey

Suits:	small craft: approx. depth of water 2'6"
Availability:	during daylight hours: key from BCA office
Restrictions:	parking at Potters Pub for patrons only
Facilities:	few facilities on canal: pub adjacent
Licence:	BCA (see above)
Charge:	included in licence fee
Directions:	follow A321 north from Farnborough and signs to Mytchett: site is north of Mytchett Lake on the east side of the canal
Link:	River Wey

Suits:	small craft: approx. depth of water 2'6"
Availability:	during daylight hours: key from BCA office
Restrictions:	inaccessible during biennial Army/Air Show
Facilities:	parking for car and trailer
Licence:	BCA (see above)
Charge:	included in licence fee
Directions:	turn off A325 dual carriageway south of canal onto A323 towards Fleet: access to site is via one-way system just after passing under the dual carriageway
Link:	River Wey

Barley Mow Slipway, Winchfield, Hants

Suits:	small craft: approx. depth of water 2'6"
Availability:	during daylight hours: key from BCA office
Restrictions:	awkward slipway on rising ground
Facilities:	parking for car and trailer, Barley Mow Pub nearby
Licence:	BCA (see above)
Charge:	included in licence fee
Directions:	from Aldershot follow A323 west to Fleet turning off to follow signs: site is on east side of Barley Mow bridge
Link:	River Wey

Galleon Marine, Colt Hill, Odiham Hants

Tel: (0256) 703691

Suits:	craft up to 25' LOA max with suitable towing vehicle
Availability:	0900-1700 daily in summer: closed sun in winter
Restrictions:	none
Facilities:	diesel, sewage and refuse disposal, water, gas, pump-out, toilets, chandlery, small shop
Licence:	BCA (see above)
Charge:	yes
Directions:	leave M3 at junction 5, taking the A287 east and turning right at either end of the bypass into Odiham Village
Link:	River Wey

BIRMINGHAM CANAL NAVIGATIONS   BW (Midlands Region)

David Tyrrell, Bradley Lane, Bilston, West Midlands WV14 8DW

The first canal was built from Aldersley on the Staffordshire and Worcestershire Canal to Birmingham and the complex network which subsequently developed was the result of three rival companies each trying to monopolise the traffic. Over 100 miles of the network are still navigable.

M.E. Braine (Boatbuilders) Ltd. Norton Canes Dock, Lime Lane, Pelsall, West Midlands

Tel: (0543) 374888

Suits:	larger craft
Availability:	during working hours by prior arrangement
Restrictions:	no slipway: launching by crane or hoist only
Facilities:	fuel, parking for car and trailer, sewage and refuse disposal, water, overnight moorings, boatyard, cranage by arrangement
Licence:	BW
Charge:	yes
Directions:	leave M6 at junction 12 following A5 east: site is between Cannock and Brownhills
Link:	Worcs and Birmingham, Birmingham and Fazeley, Staffs and Worcs, Shropshire Union and Grand Union Canals.

The Port '86, All Saints Road, Birmingham, West Midlands

Tel: 021-551 4837

Suits:	small trailed craft
Availability:	during working hours
Restrictions:	none
Facilities:	parking for car and trailer, water, toilets, dry dock
Licence:	BW
Charge:	yes
Directions:	telephone for directions: site is on Birmingham Level off Soho Loop
Link:	Worcs and Birmingham, Birmingham and Fazeley, Staffs and Worcs, Shropshire Union and Grand Union Canals

Coombeswood Canal Trust, Hawne Basin, Hereward Rise, Halesowen, West Midlands

Tel: 021-550 1355

Suits:	all craft: 70' trolley and track available
Availability:	0900-1700 daily
Restrictions:	none
Facilities:	diesel, sewage and refuse disposal, water, gas, pump-out, toilets and showers, boatyard, DIY facilities
Licence:	BW
Charge:	yes
Directions:	from Halesowen, take the Dudley road (A459) turning right into Hereward Rise: site is at top of hill by large locked gates: ring bell or go to clubhouse
Link:	Worcs and Birmingham, Birmingham and Fazeley, Staffs and Worcs, Shropshire Union and Grand Union Canals

Brecon and Abergavenny Canal
- see page 41

10

Property Division, 7th Floor, Quay West, Trafford Wharf Road, Manchester M17 1HH
Tel: 061-872-2411

Built to transport coal from the Duke of Bridgewater's mines at Worsley to Manchester, the canal was later extended to join the Trent and Mersey Canal at Preston Brook and the Leeds and Liverpool Canal at Leigh. The canal carried commercial traffic until 1974.

Hesford Marine, Warrington Lane, Lymm, Cheshire
Tel: (0925) 754639

Suits:	all craft
Availability:	during working hours by arrangement
Restrictions:	check for availability
Facilities:	diesel, water, gas, toilets, overnight moorings, chandlery and boatyard, crane by arrangement
Licence:	BW (up to 3 days) or from Estates Officer, Manchester Ship Canal Co Tel: 061-872 7031
Charge:	yes
Directions:	leave M6 at junction 20 taking B5158 to Lymm
Link:	Trent and Mersey, Rochdale and Leeds and Liverpool Canal

Lymm Marina, Warrington Lane, Lymm, Cheshire
Tel: (0925) 752945

Suits:	shallow draught craft only
Availability:	during working hours by prior arrangement only
Restrictions:	none
Facilities:	diesel, parking for car and trailer(c), refuse disposal, water, gas, toilets, chandlery and boatyard
Licence:	BW (up to 3 days) or from Estates Officer, Manchester Ship Canal Co. Tel: 061-872 7031
Charge:	yes
Directions:	leave M6 at junction 20 taking B5158 to Lymm
Link:	Trent and Mersey, Rochdale and Leeds and Liverpool Canals

Preston Brook Marina, Preston Brook, Runcorn, Cheshire
Tel: (0928) 719081

Suits:	all craft up to 30' LOA
Availability:	during working hours by prior arrangement
Restrictions:	none
Facilities:	fuel opposite, sewage and refuse disposal, water, gas, toilets
Charge:	yes
Directions:	turn off M56 at junction 11 taking A56 to Preston Brook: site is on Runcorn Branch of canal below bridge 67
Link:	Trent and Mersey, Rochdale and Leeds and Liverpool Canals

Mike Harrison, Lock Lane, Castleford, West Yorks WF10 2LH

Constructed to improve the Calder above Wakefield, this navigation was never as successful as the Aire and Calder which it joins at Fall Ing Lock in Wakefield, running for just over 18 miles to Sowerby Bridge.

Sowerby Marine and Chandlery, Sowerby Bridge, West Yorks
Tel: (0422) 832922

Suits:	all craft up to 23' LOA
Availability:	1000-1800 mon to fri: 1000-1700 sat and sun
Restrictions:	none
Facilities:	fuel (200 yds), parking for car and trailer(c), sewage and refuse disposal, water, toilets, overnight moorings, chandlery and boatyard, engine repairs
Licence:	BW available on site
Charge:	yes
Directions:	follow A58 two miles west from Halifax
Link:	Aire and Calder Navigation, Huddersfield Broad Canal and Rochdale Canal (when opened)

Elland Wharf, Elland, West Yorks

Suits:	all craft: approx. 5' water
Availability:	0800-2000 daily
Restrictions:	get permission to launch and key from Mr. Dix, 41 Victoria Wharf or Mr. W Carey (Junior), Wharf House
Facilities:	fuel, parking for car but not trailer
Licence:	BW
Charge:	yes
Directions:	from Bradford, follow A641 south and A6025 through Elland, turning off into Gas Works Lane (off Elland Bridge) and onto Elland Wharf
Link:	Aire and Calder Navigation, Huddersfield Broad Canal and Rochdale Canal (when opened)

Savile Town Wharf (Robinson's Hire Cruisers Ltd), Dewsbury, West Yorks
Tel: (0924) 467976

Suits:	craft up to 57 ' LOA and 4' draught
Availability:	during working hours
Restrictions:	none
Facilities:	fuel, parking for car and trailer(c), refuse and sewage disposal, water, gas, pump-out, toilets and showers, overnight moorings, chandlery and boatyard with crane/winch by arrangement
Licence:	BW
Charge:	yes
Directions:	from Leeds follow A62 south, turning into Mill Street East in Dewsbury: site is on the Dewsbury Arm
Link:	Aire and Calder Navigation, Huddersfield Broad Canal and Rochdale Canal (when opened)

Hugh Ross, Canal Office, Seaport Marina, Muirtown Basin, Inverness IV3 5LS
Tel: (0463) 233140

The canal runs across Scotland for 60 miles from Fort William on the west coast to
Inverness on the east coast, giving access to Loch Lochy, Loch Oich and Loch Ness.
There is a speed limit of 6mph on the canal sections.

Caley Marina, Canal Road, Inverness
Tel: (0463) 236539

Suits:	craft up to 21' LOA
Availability:	0830-1730 mon to sat: at other times by prior arrangement
Restrictions:	fairly steep slipway into 6' water
Facilities:	diesel, parking for car and trailer(c), toilets, overnight moorings, chandlery and boatyard with crane by arrangement, engine repairs
Licence:	BW available on site
Charge:	yes
Directions:	leave A9 following signs for the A862 across Inverness to Muirtown swing bridge: turn up Canal Road by the flight of locks
Link:	Moray Firth and Lock Linnhe

Seaport Marina, Muirtown Wharf, Inverness
Tel: (0463) 233140

Suits:	all craft
Availability:	0800-1800 daily
Restrictions:	steep slipway into 5' water
Facilities:	diesel on site, petrol (.25 mile), toilets
Licence:	BW licence
Charge:	yes
Directions:	turn right before Muirtown Bridge on the old A9 Beauly Road
Link:	Moray Firth and Loch Linnhe

Tomnahurich Bridge, Inverness

Suits:	all craft
Availability:	0800-1800 daily
Restrictions:	steep slipway into 5' water
Facilities:	fuel (.25 mile)
Licence:	BW licence
Charge:	yes
Directions:	turn right off the A82 at Tomnahurich Bridge
Link:	Moray Firth and Loch Linnhe

Tel: (08093) 223

Suits:	all craft
Availability:	0900-2100 daily
Restrictions:	steep slipway into approx. 4' water
Facilities:	no fuel, parking for car and trailer(c), water, toilets, overnight moorings, boatyard, restaurant, self-catering accommodation
Licence:	no licence required for Loch Oich but is required for canal
Charge:	yes
Directions:	follow A82 from Fort William 22 miles towards Inverness turning right just before South Laggan swing bridge: site is at south west end of Loch Oich

CHELMER AND BLACKWATER NAVIGATION – Chelmer and Blackwater Navigation Ltd.

Paper Mill Lock, Little Baddow, Chelmsford, Essex CM3 4BF
Tel: (0245) 412025

Until 1974 this was a working canal and is still owned by the company which founded it in 1793. The canal links Chelmsford to the sea at Maldon, a distance of 14 miles. There is a speed limit of 4mph.

Paper Mill Lock, Little Baddow, Chelmsford, Essex
Tel: (0245) 412025

Suits:	craft up to 60' LOA, 12' beam and 3' draught
Availability:	by arrangement
Restrictions:	none
Facilities:	fuel (3 miles), parking for car and trailer by arrangement
Licence:	from Chelmer and Blackwater Navigation Ltd
Charge:	yes
Directions:	from A12, take A414 to Maldon, turning left at Danbury Green to Little Baddow and going down the hill for two and a half miles: lock house yard is just before the river bridge
Link:	Blackwater estuary and North Sea

CHESTERFIELD CANAL   BW (North East Region)

John Nuttall, Dun Street, Swinton, Mexborough, South Yorks S64 8AR
Tel: (0709) 582770

The canal was originally built to facilitate the transport of goods from the Chesterfield area to the sea via the River Trent and ran from Chesterfield to West Stockwith where it joined the river. The navigable section now runs from Worksop to West Stockwith, a distance of 25.5 miles: the river lock is manned Tel: (0427) 890204 and is normally accessible from 2.5 hours before to 4.5 hours after HW. There is a speed limit of 4mph on the canal.

West Stockwith Basin, West Stockwith, Nr. Doncaster, Notts

Suits:	craft up to 55' LOA
Availability:	during daylight hours by prior arrangement with lock keeper
Restrictions:	BW key required for access
Facilities:	diesel, parking for car and trailer, gas, toilets
Licence:	BW
Charge:	yes
Directions:	turn off A631 west of Gainsborough onto A161 Goole road turning right to West Stockwith after passing through Misterton
Link:	River Trent, Humber Estuary and the North Sea

Drakeholes Tunnel, Wiseton, Notts

Suits:	all craft
Availability:	during daylight hours
Restrictions:	BW key required for access
Facilities:	no fuel, parking for car and trailer, pub nearby
Licence:	BW licence
Charge:	no
Directions:	turn off A631 Gainsborough to Bawtry road
Link:	River Trent, Humber Estuary and the North Sea

Retford and Worksop Boat Club, Clayworth Wharf, Clayworth, Notts

Suits:	all craft
Availability:	during daylight hours
Restrictions:	private club site: ask politely for use
Facilities:	club is based at old pub: water, toilets
Licence:	BW licence
Charge:	yes
Directions:	turn off A631 west of Gainsborough south onto B1403 to Clayworth: site is by Clayworth Bridge
Link:	River Trent, Humber Estuary and the North Sea

Retford, Notts (Retford Mariners Boat Club)

Suits:	all powered craft
Availability:	during daylight hours
Restrictions:	private site: seek permission before launching
Facilities:	fuel, parking for car and trailer, toilets, chandlery from Ultra Marine, Bridgegate
Licence:	BW licence
Charge:	yes
Directions:	turn left off A638 London Road at lights, going down Albert Road opposite the Albert pub
Link:	River Trent, Humber Estuary and North Sea

COVENTRY CANAL

Roger Harrington, Maintenance Yard, Atherstone Road, Hartshill, Nuneaton, Warks CV10 0TB
Tel: (0203) 392250

This canal runs for 38 miles from Coventry Basin to Fradley Junction and was built to connect Coventry with the Trent and Mersey Canal and to provide cheap coal from Bedworth coalfield. This was one of the most prosperous canals having links with the Trent and Mersey, the Birmingham and Fazeley at Fazeley Junction, the Ashby at Marston Junction and the Oxford at Hawkesbury Junction.

Club Line Cruisers, Swan Lane Wharf, Stoke Heath Coventry, West Midlands
Tel: (0203) 258864

Suits:	craft up to 20' LOA
Availability:	0900-1700 mon-fri
Restrictions:	fairly steep slipway into 2' water
Facilities:	fuel, parking for car and trailer(c), sewage and refuse disposal, water, pump-out, toilets, overnight moorings, chandlery and boatyard, engine repairs
Licence:	BW licence
Charge:	yes
Directions:	leave M6 at junction 2 taking A4600 towards City centre: after passing under railway bridge turn first right into Swan Lane
Link:	Trent and Mersey, Birmingham and Fazeley, Ashby and Oxford Canals

RIVER DEE   Council of the City of Chester

Town Hall, Chester CH1 2HN
The river is navigable from Chester to Farndon. There is a speed limit of 6mph

Dee Fords, Sandy Lane, Chester, Cheshire

Suits:	small craft
Availability:	during daylight hours
Restrictions:	all mechanically or electrically propelled boats must be registered with the Director of Environmental Health, 16 Whitefriars
Facilities:	no fuel, parking for car and trailer(c), toilets, chandlery from Chester Boat Chandlers, 31, Christleton Road
Licence:	from the Director of Environmental Health
Charge:	yes
Directions:	follow B5130 one and a half miles south from Chester
Link:	none

Rosebank House, Main Street, Camelon, Falkirk FK1 4DS
Tel: (0324) 612415

Originally built to link the Firth of Clyde on the West Coast and the Firth of Forth on the East Coast, the canal is now obstructed by road crossings but reasonable lengths are available for cruising. There is a speed limit of 6mph.

Hay's Slip, Southbank Road, Kirkintilloch, Strathclyde

Suits: all craft: large slip with good surface
Availability: during daylight hours
Restrictions: canal navigable for 6 miles: height restriction 6'
Facilities: petrol, parking for car and trailer
Licence: BW licence from Canal Office
Charge: no
Directions: follow the A803 from Glasgow to Kirkintilloch
Link: none

Stables Inn, Glasgow Road Bridge, Kirkintilloch, Strathclyde

Tel: 0836-704 287 (Canalside Leisure Ltd),

Suits: all craft: large slipway with rails and boat trolley and small ramp
Availability: during daylight hours
Restrictions: canal navigable to Maryhill (6.5 miles): height restriction 6'
Facilities: petrol, parking for car and trailer
Licence: BW licence from Canal Office
Charge: yes
Directions: follow A803 one and a half miles west of Kirkintilloch
Link: none

Sandbank Street, Maryhill, Strathclyde

Suits: craft up to 13' LOA
Availability: during daylight hours
Restrictions: access ramp is quite steep. Canal is navigable to Kirkintilloch (6.5 miles): height restriction 6'
Facilities: no fuel
Licence: BW licence from Canal Office
Charge: no charge
Directions: follow A81 north west from Glasgow
Link: none

Firhill Basin

Suits: craft up to 13' LOA
Availability: during daylight hours
Restrictions: contact canal foreman for key Tel: 041-332 1065: site gives access to one mile canal
Facilities: no fuel, parking for car and trailer

Licence:	BW licence from Canal Office
Charge:	no charge
Directions:	access is via Firhill Road, site is adjacent road bridge
Link:	none

Old Basin Works, Hamiltonhill, Strathclyde

Suits:	all craft
Availability:	during daylight hours
Restrictions:	access and slipway are rough: site is only suitable for 4-wheel drive vehicles: contact canal foreman Tel: 041-332 1065
Facilities:	no fuel
Licence:	BW licence from Canal Office
Charge:	no charge
Directions:	from canal foreman (see above)
Link:	none

Auchinstarry, nr Kilsyth, Strathclyde

Suits:	craft up to 25' LOA
Availability:	during daylight hours
Restrictions:	access to four mile section of canal
Facilities:	no fuel, parking for car and trailer
Licence:	BW licence from Canal Office
Charge:	no charge
Directions:	follow A803 towards Kilsyth, turning onto B802: site is located next to BW depot and access road is immediately adjacent to bridge
Link:	none

GRAND UNION CANAL   BW (South East Region)

The system comprises at least eight separate canals which together link London with Birmingham, Leicester and Nottingham.

Brentford to Cowley – Mark Benstead, Toll House, Delamere Terrace, London W2 6ND
Tel: 071-286 6101

Willowtree Marina, West Quay Drive, Yeading, Middx
Tel: 081-841 4959

Suits:	small craft
Availability:	0800-2000 daily
Restrictions:	none
Facilities:	fuel, parking for car and trailer(c), telephone, sewage and refuse disposal, water, gas, pump-out, toilets and showers, overnight moorings, chandlery and boatyard, launderette, shop
Licence:	BW licence
Charge:	yes
Directions:	from the Hayes bypass, take the east exit into Willowtree Lane at the

Willowtree roundabout: turn into Glencoe Road going past the Tesco
Superstore and then in to West Quay Drive

Link: Grand Union Main Line, River Thames

**Cowley to Weedon - Caroline Clark, Marsworth Junction, Watery Lane,
Marsworth, Tring, Herts HP23 4LZ** Tel: (044 282) 5938

High Line Yachting Ltd. Mansion Lane, Iver, Bucks
Tel: (0753) 651476

Suits:	craft up to 25' LOA
Availability:	during working hours: closed mon
Restrictions:	none
Facilities:	diesel on site, petrol (1 mile), parking for car and trailer(c), sewage and refuse disposal, water, gas, pump-out, toilet and showers, overnight moorings, chandlery and boatyard including crane
Licence:	BW licence
Charge:	yes
Directions:	follow B470 Langley to Iver road, turning right into Mansion Lane: site is by canal bridge on lock-free three mile Slough Arm
Link:	River Thames, River Nene, River Soar; Oxford, Stratford-on-Avon and Birmingham Canals

Uxbridge Boat Centre, Uxbridge Wharf, Waterloo Road, Uxbridge, Middx
Tel: (0895) 252019

Suits:	DIY use up to approx 20' LOA
Availability:	0900-1800 tues to sat, 1100-1600 sun
Restrictions:	closed mon and sun in dec and jan: access is via narrow and congested streets
Facilities:	fuel, limited parking for car and trailer(c), refuse and sewage disposal, water, gas, toilets, overnight moorings, chandlery and boatyard
Licence:	BW
Charge:	yes
Directions:	turn off the A4007, Uxbridge to Slough road into Waterloo Road
Link:	River Thames, River Nene, River Soar; Oxford, Stratford-on-Avon and Birmingham Canals

Harefield Marina, Moorhall Road, Harefield, Middx.
Tel: (0985) 822036

Suits:	small craft
Availability:	0900-1730 daily
Restrictions:	none
Facilities:	diesel on site, petrol (1 mile), parking for car and trailer(c), toilets, chandlery and boatyard with crane
Licence:	licence
Charge:	yes
Directions:	follow A412 from the A40/M25 turning into Moorhall Road
Link:	River Thames, River Nene, River Soar; Oxford, Stratford-on-Avon and Birmingham Canals

Bridgewater Boats, Castle Wharf, Berkhamsted, Herts
Tel: (0442) 863615

Suits:	small craft
Availability:	during working hours
Restrictions:	none
Facilities:	diesel, water, gas, pump-out, toilets, overnight moorings
Licence:	BW licence
Charge:	yes
Directions:	turn off A41: site is opposite the Castle by bridge 141
Link:	River Thames, River Nene, River Soar; Oxford, Stratford-on-Avon and Birmingham Canals

Cowroast Marina, By Cowroast Lock, Tring, Herts
Tel: (044 282) 3222

Suits:	small craft
Availability:	0900-1730 daily in summer: 0900-1730 mon-fri, 1000-1630 sat and sun in winter
Restrictions:	launching by prior arrangement only
Facilities:	diesel, water, gas, pump-out, overnight moorings, chandlery, pub
Licence:	BW licence
Charge:	yes
Directions:	turn off A41, crossing canal to site by Cowroast Lock
Link:	River Thames, River Nene, River Soar; Oxford, Stratford-on-Avon and Birmingham Canals

Willowbridge Marina, Stoke Road, Bletchley, Bucks
Tel: (0908) 643242

Suits:	craft up to 15 tons
Availability:	0900-1700: closed winter weekends
Restrictions:	launching by crane only by prior arrangement
Facilities:	fuel, parking for car and trailer(c), refuse and sewage disposal, water, gas, pump-out, toilets, overnight moorings, chandlery, boatyard
Licence:	BW licence
Charge:	yes
Directions:	turn off the A5 at the roundabout south of Milton Keynes onto the A4146 following signs to Aylesbury and Leighton Buzzard
Link:	River Thames, River Nene, River Soar; Oxford, Stratford-on-Avon and Birmingham Canals

Navigation Inn, Cosgrove, Northants
Tel: (0908) 543156

Suits:	all craft
Availability:	by prior arrangement only
Restrictions:	none
Facilities:	pub, parking nearby(c); all other facilities at Cosgrove Marina
Licence:	BW licence
Charge:	yes

Directions: turn off the A508: site is between Cosgrove and Castlethorpe
Link: RiverThames, River Nene, River Soar; Oxford, Stratford-on-Avon and
               Birmingham Canals

Baxter Boatfitting Services, Yardley Gobion, Northants
Tel: (0908) 542844

Suits: craft up to 30' LOA and 7' wide
Availability: by prior arrangement
Restrictions: access limits length of craft to be launched
Facilities: diesel, refuse and sewage disposal, water, gas, pump-out, toilets,
               overnight moorings, chandlery, boatyard with crane, engine repairs
Licence: BW licence
Charge: yes
Directions: follow signs from A508 south of Northampton, site is at Yardley Wharf
Link: River Thames, River Nene, River Soar; Oxford, Stratford-on-Avon and
               Birmingham Canals

Stoke Locks, Stoke Bruerne, Northants
Tel: (044 282) 5938

Suits: all craft
Availability: during daylight hours
Restrictions: gated slipway requires BW key for access
Facilities: fuel from Yardley Wharf, parking for car and trailer in public car park
               nearby, toilets in village, chandlers and crane at Yardley Wharf
Licence: BW licence
Charge: no
Directions: leave M1 at junction 15 taking A508 south: site is where road crosses
               canal between locks 19 and 20
Link: River Thames, River Nene, River Soar; Oxford, Stratford-on-Avon and
               Birmingham Canals

BW Gayton Yard, Blisworth, Northants
Tel: (044 282) 5938

Suits: craft up to 30' LOA
Availability: during daylight hours: check for availability
Restrictions: steep slipway
Facilities: fuel, no parking, telephone, refuse and sewage disposal, water,
               overnight moorings, toilets, chandlery and boatyard nearby
Licence: BW licence
Charge: no
Directions: turn off A43 south of Northampton following signs to Gayton: further
               directions can be obtained from yard by sending a sae.
Link: RiverThames, River Nene, River Soar; Oxford, Stratford-on-Avon and
               Birmingham Canals

Concoform Marine, The Boatyard, High Street, Weedon, Northants
Tel: (0327) 40739

Suits:	all craft
Availability:	during working hours tues-sat in summer, mon-fri in winter
Restrictions:	none
Facilities:	fuel, water, gas, pump-out, overnight moorings
Licence:	BW licence
Charge:	yes
Directions:	leave M1 at junction 16 following A45 to Weedon
Link:	River Thames, River Nene, River Soar; Oxford, Stratford-on-Avon and Birmingham Canals

Whilton Marina, Whilton Locks, Whilton, Daventry, Northants
Tel: (0327) 842577

Suits:	all craft
Availability:	0900-1800 daily
Restrictions:	none
Facilities:	fuel, parking for car and trailer(c), sewage disposal, water, gas, toilets and showers, overnight moorings, engine repairs
Licence:	BW licence
Charge:	yes
Directions:	leave M1 at junction 16 following A45 and A5 north: site is three miles north of Weedon
Link:	River Thames, River Nene, River Soar; Oxford, Stratford-on-Avon and Birmingham Canals

Welton Hythe, Welton, Daventry, Northants (Weltonfield Narrowboats)
Tel: (0327) 842282

Suits:	narrowboats and cabin cruisers
Availability:	during daylight hours
Restrictions:	none
Facilities:	fuel (1 mile), parking for car and trailer(c), telephone, sewage and refuse disposal, water, gas, pump-out, toilets, overnight moorings, chandlery and boatyard, engine repairs
Licence:	BW licence
Charge:	yes
Directions:	site is on the A5, one mile south of the junction with the B4036
Link:	Grand Union Main Line and Soar Navigation

North Kilworth Narrow Boats, Kilworth Marina, North Kilworth, Leics
Tel:(0858) 880484

Suits:	craft up to 20' LOA and 6'10" wide
Availability:	0900-1700 mon to sat, sun in season 1000-1700
Restrjctions:	slipway is steep but level at bottom
Facilities:	fuel, parking for car and trailer(c), sewage and refuse disposal, water, gas, pump-out, toilets and showers, overnight moorings, boatyard
Licence:	BW licence

Charge: yes
Directions: turn off M1 at junction 20 taking A427 east: site is between North
               Kilworth and Husbands Bosworth
Link: Grand Union Main Line and Soar Navigation

GRAND UNION   Leicester Section

Market Harborough to River Trent - Richard Sawicki, Canal Wharf, Derby Road,
Loughborough, Leics LE11 0BX
Tel: (0509) 212729

Anglo-Welsh Canal Holidays, The Canal Basin, Market Harborough, Leics
Tel: (0858) 466910

Suits: dinghies only
Availability: 0800-1700 daily
Restrictions: slipway stops at water: retrieval is difficult
Facilities: fuel, sewage and refuse disposal, water, gas, pump-out, (mon-fri), toi-
               lets, chandlery and boatyard
Licence: BW licence
Charge: yes
Directions: turn off A6 in Market Harborough:site is on five and a half mile long
               Market Harborough Arm
Link: Grand Union Main Line and Soar Navigation

Foxton Boat Services, Bottom Lock, Foxton, Market Harborough, Leics
Tel: (0533) 792285

Suits: small craft up to approx 25' LOA
Availability: 0900-1100 summer, 0900-1700 winter
Restrictions: none
Facilities: fuel, parking for car and trailer(c), sewage and refuse disposal, water,
               gas, pump-out, toilets and showers, overnight moorings, chandlery
               and boatyard with crane, engine repairs
Licence: BW licence
Charge: yes
Directions: turn off A6 onto A508: site is signposted from there
Link: Grand Union Main Line and Soar Navigation

Leicester Marina, Old Bridge, Thurcaston Road, Leicester, Leics
Tel: (0533) 662194

Suits: craft up to 25' LOA: also access for launching lorry-borne boats up to
               70' LOA and 14' beam and crane support pads to 50 tons
Availability: by prior arrangement only
Restrictions: steep slipway (1:5)
Facilities: diesel on site, petrol from garage nearby, parking for car and trailer(c),
               sewage disposal, water, gas, pump-out, toilets, chandlery and boat-
               yard with crane
Licence: BW licence available on site

Charge:	yes
Directions:	turn off M1 at junction 21 onto A563 distributor road clockwise: carry on through Braunstone Town (Leicester west) until Red Hill flyover is reached and marina is visible; entrance is from Thurcaston Road
Link:	Grand Union, Main Line and Soar Navigation

Old Junction Boatyard, Meadow Lane, Syston, Leics
Tel: (0533) 692135

Suits:	craft up to 27' LOA
Availability:	0900-1800 daily
Restrictions:	none
Facilities:	diesel, parking for car and trailer(c), refuse and sewage disposal, water, gas, toilets, chandlery and boatyard, engine repairs
Licence:	BW licence
Charge:	yes
Directions:	follow A46 and A607 north from Leicester: access to site is from B6670
Link:	Grand Union Main Line and Soar Navigation

Sileby Mill Boatyard, Mill Lane, Sileby, Leics
Tel: (0509) 813404

Suits:	all craft
Availability:	during daylight hours
Restrictions:	wide trailers may have difficulty getting through gate
Facilities:	diesel, petrol (.5 mile), parking for car and trailer, sewage and refuse disposal, water, gas, pump-out, toilets, overnight moorings, limited chandlery, boatyard, engine repairs
Licence:	BW licence
Charge:	yes
Directions:	situated just off B674 between Mountsorrel on the A6 and Sileby
Link:	Grand Union Main Line and Soar Navigation

Braunston Marina Ltd, Braunston, Nr Daventry, Northants
Tel: (0788) 891373

Suits:	craft up to 25' LOA
Availability:	0900-1700 daily
Restrictions:	none
Facilities:	fuel, parking for car and trailer(c), sewage and refuse disposal, water, gas, pump-out, toilets, overnight moorings, chandlery and boatyard, crane by arrangement
Licence:	BW licence
Charge:	yes
Directions:	turn off A45 three miles west of Daventry: site is just outside Braunston
Link:	River Thames, River Nene, River Soar

GRAND UNION

Napton to Camp Hill - Tom Brock, White House, Canal Lane, Hatton, Warks
Tel: (0926) 492192

Calcutt Marina, Stockton, Nr. Rugby, Warks

Tel: (092 681) 3757

Suits:	all craft
Availability:	0900-1700 daily
Restrictions:	none
Facilities:	diesel, petrol (.5 mile), parking for car and trailer(c), sewage and refuse disposal, water, gas, pump-out, toilets, overnight moorings, chandlery, boatyard, crane by arrangement, engine repairs
Licence:	BW licence
Charge:	yes
Directions:	turn off A425 at Napton taking the Broadwell road: site is on right-hand side, half a mile on from Crossroads Garage
Link:	River Thames, River Nene, River Soar

GRANTHAM CANAL

Richard Mercer, 24 Meadow Lane, Nottingham NG2 3HL
Tel: (0602) 862411

Built from Grantham to the River Trent at Trent Bridge, Nottingham, a three mile section of the canal, which it is hoped to extend soon, is now navigable. Further information from Mr C Tizzard, Publicity Officer for the Grantham Canal Restoration Society Tel: (0602) 400181.

Denton Wharf, Denton, nr Grantham, Lincs

Suits:	all trailable craft
Availability:	during daylight hours
Restrictions:	slipway is fairly steep
Facilities:	parking for car and trailer, picnic site
Licence:	BW licence
Charge:	no
Directions:	from A1 take A607 towards Melton Mowbray, turning right into Denton Village and bearing right again in the village to get to the wharf which is at the end of the farm road by a red brick hump-backed bridge
Link:	none

This site was the winner of the BMIF Slipways Award Scheme in 1990. The National Trailboat Festival is to be held at Woolsthorpe by Belvoir in May'94 and it is hoped that by then, the canal will be navigable from there to Denton.

HUDDERSFIELD BROAD CANAL   BW (North West Region)

Ian Fullerton, Vesta Street, Ancoats, Manchester M4 6DS
Tel: 061-273 4686

This canal leaves the Calder and Hebble at Cooper Bridge, running for three and a half miles to Huddersfield where it connects with the Huddersfield Narrow Canal. Aspley Basin is the limit of navigation for craft with a beam greater than 7'. There is a speed limit of 4 knots.

Aspley Wharf Marina, Aspley Basin, Huddersfield, West Yorks
Tel: (0484) 514123

Suits:	craft up to 25' LOA
Availability:	during working hours
Restrictions:	BW key required to open Turnbridge Loco Lift Bridge
Facilities:	fuel, parking for cars(c), sewage and refuse disposal, water, gas, overnight moorings, chandlery and boatyard, engine repairs
Licence:	BW licence
Charge:	yes
Directions:	on main A642 Wakefield Road
Link:	Calder and Hebble, Huddersfield Narrow Canal

HUDDERSFIELD NARROW CANAL   Huddersfield Canal Society

239 Mossley Road, Ashton-under-Lyne, Lancs OL6 6LN
Tel: 061-339 1332

Built to give a through route across the Pennines, this canal fell into disuse.Restoration work is still in progress and navigable sections do not at present connect. The lower end of the canal, between Aspley Basin and just below Stanley Dawson Lock is now accessible and it is hoped the section to Slaithwaite will be navigable in the near future.

Huddersfield Polytechnic, Wakefield Road, Huddersfield, West Yorks

Suits:	craft up to 20' LOA
Availability:	during daylight hours
Restrictions:	contact Pro Rector, Huddersfield Polytechnic, Greensgate before launching
Facilities:	fuel, parking for car and trailer(c), toilets
Licence:	BW licence
Charge:	yes
Directions:	site is adjacent A629 Wakefield Road
Link:	short section of Huddersfield Narrow Canal: Huddersfield Broad Canal and Calder and Hebble Navigation

Wool Road Car Park, Uppermill, Oldham, Lancs

Suits:	craft up to 26' LOA
Availability:	1000-1600 daily
Restrictions:	none
Facilities:	fuel, parking for car and trailer, toilets (100 yds)
Licence:	BW licence
Charge:	no
Directions:	turn off A670 Wood Road into public car park
Link:	access to half a mile navigable section of canal and two locks

Slaithwaite, West Yorks

Suits:	craft up to 12' LOA
Availability:	1000-1600 daily
Restrictions:	none
Facilities:	fuel, parking for car and trailer, toilets
Licence:	BW licence
Charge:	no
Directions:	turn off A62 Manchester Road in town centre into Britannia Road
Link:	access to two and a half mile section of canal between Marsden and Slaithwaite including 18 locks

KENNET AND AVON CANAL   BW (South West Region)

Terry Kemp, The Locks, Bath Road, Devizes, Wilts SN10 1HB
Tel: (0380) 722859

The canal was built from Newbury to Bath to link two rivers, the Kennet and the Avon. With its connection with the Thames at Reading, the resulting canal became a through route to London but never became very prosperous, falling into disuse in the 1950's. The canal has now been restored throughout, enabling boats to navigate from Reading to Bath and Bristol. However, limited water supply in some sections may restrict the use of lock flights, in particular at Crofton and Devizes. There is a speed limit of 4mph.

Greenham Island, Mill Lane, Newbury, Berks (Newbury Boat Co)
Tel: (0635) 42884

Suits:	canal cruisers up to 25' LOA
Availability:	0900-1700 by arrangement only
Restrictions:	booking is essential
Facilities:	diesel, petrol (.5 mile), parking for car and trailer(c), sewage and refuse disposal, water, gas, pump-out, overnight moorings, boatyard,
Licence:	BW licence
Charge:	yes
Directions:	leave M4 at junction 13 taking the A34 south and turning left at the second roundabout into Mill Lane: take first right by Greenham Mill housing complex and head for the canal bank and gateway on left

Pewsey Wharf, Pewsey, Wilts (Kennet and Avon Trust)
Tel: (067) 262147

Suits:	craft up to 23' LOA, 9'6" width
Availability:	0900-1800 daily
Restrictions:	bumpy surface on slipway
Facilities:	fuel (3 miles), parking for car and trailer (ask Warden), telephone, toilets, pub nearby, repairs from Gibsons Boat Services, Honey Street, Pewsey
Licence:	BW licence
Charge:	no
Directions:	follow A345 south from Marlborough
Link:	River Thames, River Avon and Bristol Channel

Devizes Wharf, Devizes, Wilts (Kennet and Avon Trust)
Tel: (0380) 721279/729489

Suits:	craft up to 23'LOA
Availability:	during daylight hours
Restrictions:	steep and narrow slipway
Facilities:	fuel, parking for car and trailer(c), telephone, water, toilets, shop
Licence:	BW licence
Charge:	no
Directions:	follow signs from town centre
Link:	River Thames, River Avon and Bristol Channel

Foxhanger Wharf, Lower Foxhanger, Devizes, Wilts
Tel: (0380) 828254

Suits:	all craft up to 23' LOA
Availability:	during daylight hours: please telephone or call at Lower Foxhangers Farm before using slip
Restrictions:	none; assistance available by arrangement
Facilities:	fuel from Devizes (2 miles), parking for car and trailer(c), telephone and toilet (300 yds), chandlery from Wharfside Chandlery, Devizes (2 miles), repairs from Nelcris Marine, Foxhanger Wharf
Licence:	BW licence
Charge:	yes
Directions:	turn into farm entrance (signed Lower Foxhanger Farm) on north side A361, half a mile east of junction of A361 and A365 and two miles west of Devizes: site is immediately below the Caen Hill flight
Link:	River Thames, River Avon and Bristol Channel

Tranquil Boats, Lock House, Semington, Trowbridge, Wilts
Tel: (0380) 870654

Suits:	craft up to 23' LOA
Availability:	during daylight hours by arrangement only
Restrictions:	none
Facilities:	diesel from Hilperton, petrol in village, parking for car and trailer(c), tractor available for assistance

Licence:	BW licence
Charge:	yes
Directions:	turn off A350, two miles south of Melksham
Link:	River Thames, River Avon and Bristol Channel

Hilperton Marine, Hilperton Wharf, Hammond Way, Trowbridge, Wilts
Tel: (0225) 765243

Suits:	craft up to 23' LOA
Availability:	during daylight hours
Restrictions:	none
Facilities;	fuel, parking for car and trailer(c), telephone, sewage and refuse disposal, water, gas, pump-out, toilets, moorings, chandlery and boatyard, bar and restaurant and children's play area
Licence:	BW licence available on site
Charge:	yes
Directions:	the B3106 from Trowbridge passes the marina
Link:	River Thames, River Avon and Bristol Channel

Bradford-on-Avon Marina, Trowbridge Road, Widbrook, Bradford-on-Avon, Wilts
Tel: (0225) 864562

Suits:	all trailed craft: larger boats can be launched by crane
Availability:	0830-1700 mon-sat by prior arrangement
Restrictions:	steep slipway
Facilities:	diesel, parking for car and trailer, sewage disposal, water, gas, chandlery and restaurant
Licence:	BW licence
Charge:	yes
Directions:	turn off the A363 Bradford-on-Avon to Trowbridge Road
Link:	River Thames, River Avon and Bristol Channel

Bradford-on-Avon Wharf, Frome Road, Bradford-on-Avon, Wilts
Tel: (0380) 721279 (Kennet and Avon Trust)

Suits:	craft up to 23' LOA
Availability:	0800-1800 daily
Restrictions:	steep slipway with hand winch and drop at end into 4' water
Facilities:	fuel, limited parking for car and trailer(c), telephone, toilets, shop
Licence:	BW licence
Charge:	yes
Directions:	follow the A3109 south from Bradford-on-Avon: site is at lock 14
Link:	River Thames, River Avon and Bristol Channel

Brass Knocker Bottom Boatyard, Monkton Combe, Bath, Avon (Bath and Dundas Canal Company)

Tel: (0225) 722292

Suits:	craft up to 23' LOA and 6'10" wide
Availability:	during working hours by prior arrangement only
Restrictions:	stop lock at canal entrance limits boat width
Facilities:	diesel, petrol (2 miles), parking for car and trailer(c), telephone, refuse and sewage disposal, water, gas, pump-out, toilets and boatyard
Licence:	BW licence available on site
Charge:	yes
Directions:	site is on Somerset Coal Canal at junction of A36 and B3108
Link:	River Thames, River Avon and Bristol Channel

LANCASTER CANAL   BW (North West Region)

Terry Horan, Aldcliffe Road, Lancaster LA1 1SU
Tel: (0524) 32712

Built to improve access from Lancaster to Preston and thence to Wigan and Manchester it is now navigable for just over 40 miles from Preston to Carnforth: the only access to the sea is via the Glasson Branch and there is no junction with the Ribble. There is a speed limit of 4mph.

Adventure Cruisers, Canal Wharf, Catforth, Preston, Lancs

Tel: (0772) 690232

Suits:	craft up to 25' LOA
Availability:	by prior arrangement only
Restrictions:	BW key needed for locks on canal: access is narrow and winding and slipway steep but Land Rover always available to assist
Facilities:	diesel, petrol (.5 mile), parking for car and trailer(c), water, gas, pump-out, toilets and showers, overnight moorings, chandlery, boatyard, tea shop
Licence:	BW licence available on site
Charge:	yes
Directions:	turn off A6 at Broughton onto the B5269 westwards: fork left at junction following signs to Catforth, turning left in village and site is on left before canal bridge (Swillbrook bridge 32)
Link:	Lancaster Canal, Glasson Branch and sea

Marina Park, Canal Wharf, Galgate, Lancs
Tel: (0524) 751368

Suits:	craft up to 60' LOA
Availability:	during working hours by prior arrangement
Restrictions:	BW key needed for locks on canal
Facilities:	fuel, parking for car and trailer(c), refuse and sewage disposal, water, gas, toilets and showers, chandlery, boatyard with crane and winch
Licence:	BW licence
Charge:	yes
Directions:	leave M6 at junction 33 taking A6 towards Lancaster
Link:	Lancaster Canal, Glasson Branch and sea

Glasson Basin Yacht Co, Glasson Dock, Lancs
Tel: (0524) 751491

Suits:	all craft
Availability:	by prior arrangement only
Restrictions:	locks on Glasson Branch take boats up to 72' LOA: 24 hours notice is required to lock out into Glasson Dock Tel: (0524) 751566
Facilities:	fuel, parking for car and trailer(c), refuse and sewage disposal, water, gas, toilets and showers, moorings, chandlery, boatyard with crane and winch, engine repairs
Licence:	BW licence
Charge:	yes
Directions:	turn off M6 at junction 34 taking A588 and B5290
Link:	Lancaster Canal and open sea via Glasson Dock

Nu-Way Acorn, Lundsfield, Carnforth, Lancs
Tel: (0524) 734457

Suits:	all craft
Availability:	during working hours
Restrictions:	none
Facilities:	fuel, parking for car and trailer(c), telephone, refuse disposal, overnight moorings, boatyard, engine repairs
Licence:	BW licence
Charge:	yes
Directions:	turn off M6 at junction 35, taking A6 to Carnforth
Link:	Lancaster Canal, Glasson Branch and sea

LEE AND STORT NAVIGATION   BW (South East Region)

Michael Render, Enfield Lock. Ordnance Road, Enfield, Middx
Tel: (0992) 764626

The River Lee (Lea) is navigable for almost 28 miles from Limehouse Basin to Hertford. The river can also be entered from Bow Creek via Bow Locks or from the Regent's Canal via the Hertford Union Canal. The junction with the River Stort, which is canalised for nearly 14 miles to Bishop's Stortford, is at Fielde's Weir. There is a speed limit of 4mph.

Springfield Marina, Spring Hill, Clapton, London E5
Tel: 081-806 1717

Suits:	craft up to 36' LOA
Availability:	0835-1700 daily
Restrictions:	access via unmade track
Facilities:	diesel, parking for car and trailer(c), telephone, sewage and refuse disposal, water, gas, pump-out, toilet and showers, overnight moorings, boatyard with boat lift (up to 25')
Licence:	BW licence
Charge:	yes
Directions:	turn off A104 Lea Bridge Road in Leyton: marina is on east bank
Link:	River Thames and canal network

Page and Hewitt Ltd, The Boathouse, Stonebridge Lock, Marsh Lane, Tottenham, London N17
Tel: 081-801 2571

Suits:	craft up to 20' LOA
Availability:	0900-1700 daily
Restrictions:	none
Facilities:	diesel, parking for car and trailer, telephone, refuse disposal, water, gas, pump-out, toilets and showers, boatyard with crane, cafe
Licence:	BW licence
Charge:	yes
Directions:	turn into Watermead Way from Tottenham Hale and site is signposted
Link:	River Thames and canal network

Hazlemere Marina, High Bridge Street, Waltham Abbey, Essex
Tel: (0992) 711863

Suits:	craft up to 24' LOA and 8' beam
Availability:	daily during daylight hours
Restrictions:	none
Facilities:	petrol (.25 mile), parking for car and trailer(c), telephone, sewage and refuse disposal, water, toilets, overnight moorings, cafe
Licence:	BW licence
Charge:	yes
Directions:	turn off M25 at junction 26 following A121 west: access to site is from High Bridge Street
Link:	River Thames and canal network

Old Mill Meadows, Mill Lane, Broxbourne, Herts,
Tel: (0992) 461951

Suits:	craft up to 16' LOA
Availability:	0900-1800 daily
Restrictions:	obtain key from Warden
Facilities:	parking for car and trailer, toilets, refuse and sewage disposal, water, pump-out and overnight moorings at Broxbourne Boat Centre

Licence:	BW licence
Charge:	yes
Directions:	from A10, take A1170 into Broxbourne, turning right at traffic lights into Station Road and then right into Mill Lane
Link:	River Thames and canal network

Rye House Quay, Rye Road, Hoddesdon, Herts

Tel: (0920) 870499

Suits:	craft up to 20' LOA
Availability:	0900-1800 daily
Restrictions:	none
Facilities:	parking for car and trailer, telephone, toilets
Licence:	BW licence
Charge:	yes
Directions:	from A10 take the A1170 turning to Hoddesdon then follow signs to Rye Park
Link:	River Thames and canal network

Stanstead Abbots Marina, South Street, Stanstead Abbots, Herts

Tel: (0920) 870499

Suits:	craft up to 25' LOA with max 5' draught
Availability:	0900-1700 daily (except sun nov-mar)
Restrictions:	none
Facilities:	diesel, petrol (.25 mile), parking for car and trailer(c), telephone, refuse and sewage disposal, water, pump-out, toilets and showers, overnight moorings, chandlery, boatyard with crane, engine repairs
Licence:	BW licence
Charge:	yes
Directions:	from A10, take A414 into Stanstead Abbots, turning off into South Street
Link:	River Thames and canal network

LEEDS AND LIVERPOOL CANAL BW (North West Region)

West – (Greenberfield to Liverpool) Ian Selby, Pottery Road, Wigan, Lancs WN3 5AA Tel: (0942) 42239

East – (Greenberfield to Leeds) David Blackburn, Dobson Lock, Annerley Bridge, Bradford, West Yorks BD10 OPY Tel: (0274) 611303

The longest canal built by one company, this canal is 127 miles long. It connects Leeds to the River Mersey at Liverpool via the Stanley Dock Branch, the Ribble Estuary at Tarleton via the Rufford Branch and the Bridgewater Canal via the Leigh Branch. In Leeds the canal connects with the Aire and Calder Navigation at River Lock.

The Lathom Slipway, Crabtree Lane, Burscough, Lancs

Tel: (0704) 893312

Suits:	craft up to 30' LOA and 9' wide
Availability:	mornings and late afternoons or by prior arrangement
Restrictions:	none
Facilities:	fuel (1 mile), parking for car and trailer by arrangement, overnight moorings, pub; chandlery, water, gas from Lathom Marine
Licence:	yes
Charge:	yes
Directions:	turn off A59 on south side of canal into Higgins Lane, turning right into Crabtree Lane: site is at pub by bridge 32
Link:	River Mersey, River Douglas/Ribble, Aire and Calder, Bridgewater Canal

James Mayor, The Boatyard, Tarleton, Nr. Preston, Lancs

Tel: (0772) 812250

Suits:	all craft (slipway up to 90' LOA)
Availability:	during daylight hours
Restrictions:	Rufford Branch can only be entered or left via Tarleton Lock at HW
Facilities:	diesel, parking for car and trailer, telephone, sewage and refuse disposal, water, gas, pump-out, toilets and showers, overnight moorings, chandlery, boatyard, 3-ton crane and winch, engine repairs
Licence:	BW licence for canal, no licence for river
Charge:	yes
Directions:	from junction of A59 and A565 take Church Road through village then down Plox Brow and along canal bank: site is on Rufford Branch
Link:	Leeds and Liverpool Canal and River Douglas via Tarleton Lock

White Bear Marina, Park Road, Adlington, Nr. Chorley, Lancs

Tel: (0257) 481054

Suits:	craft up to 45' LOA and 10' wide
Availability:	0900-1200, 1300-1800 mon-fri, 1000-1800 sat-sun
Restrictions:	none
Facilities:	fuel, parking for car and trailer(c), telephone, refuse and sewage disposal, water, gas, pump-out, toilets and showers, overnight moorings, chandlery, boatyard, engine repairs
Licence:	BW licence
Charge:	yes
Directions:	leave M61 northbound at junction 6 taking A6 north for 2 miles to Adlington or leave M6 at junction 27 following signs to Standish, then Chorley, then A6 towards Manchester, turning off in Adlington
Link:	River Mersey, River Douglas/Ribble, Aire and Calder, Bridgewater Canal

Hapton Boatyard, 95 Manchester Road, Hapton, Burnley, Lancs
Tel: (0282) 73178

Suits:	all craft launched by 15 ton mobile crane
Availability:	by prior arrangement
Restrictions:	no slipway
Facilities:	diesel, refuse disposal, water, gas, overnight moorings, boatyard, engine repairs
Licence:	BW licence
Charge:	none
Directions:	turn off the M65 at junction 8 taking the A56 and A679
Link:	River Mersey, River Douglas/Ribble, Aire and Calder, Bridgewater Canal

BW Yard, Finsley Gate, Burnley, Lancs
Tel: (0282) 428680

Suits:	craft up to 25' LOA
Availability:	at all times
Restrictions:	by prior arrangement
Facilities:	telephone, refuse and sewage disposal, water, gas, pump-out, toilets, overnight moorings, toilet
Licence:	BW licence
Charge:	yes
Directions:	leave Burnley town centre by Manchester road
Link:	River Mersey, River Douglas/Ribble, Aire and Calder, Bridgewater Canal

Silsden Boats, The Wharf, Silsden, Nr. Keighly, West Yorks
Tel: (0535) 653675

Suits:	craft up to 60' LOA
Availability:	0800-1730 mon-fri and sun
Facilities:	diesel, parking for car and trailer by arrangement, refuse disposal, water, gas, pump-out, boatyard
Licence:	BW licence
Charge:	yes
Directions:	turn off A629 north of Keighly onto the A6034: site is approached via Elliott Street
Link:	River Mersey, River Douglas/Ribble, Aire and Calder, Bridgewater Canal

Hainsworths Boatyard, Fairfax Road, Bingley, West Yorks
Tel: (0274) 565925

Suits:	small craft only
Availability:	0830-2200 summer, 0830-1700 winter
Restrictions:	none
Facilities:	fuel, parking for car and trailer(c), telephone, water, gas, pump-out, toilets, overnight moorings, chandlery, boatyard
Licence:	BW licence

Charge:	yes
Directions:	approach on A650 Keighley/Bradford road, turning at main traffic lights in Bingley up Park Road towards Eldwick. After half a mile turn left into Hall Bank Drive, left at end into Beck Lane and straight over roundabout: yard is at very end on left just above Five Rise Locks
Link:	River Mersey, River Douglas/Ribble, Aire and Calder, Bridgewater Canal

Rodley Boat Centre, Canal Wharf, Canal Road, Rodley, West Yorks
Tel: (0532) 576132

Suits:	all craft
Availability:	0900-dusk daily
Restrictions:	fairly steep slipway
Facilities:	fuel, parking for car and trailer (c), refuse and sewage disposal, water, gas, pump-out, toilets, overnight moorings, chandlery, boatyard
Licence:	BW licence
Charge:	yes
Directions:	site is off Leeds Outer Ring Road and adjacent A657, by bridge 216A
Link:	River Mersey, River Douglas/Ribble, Aire and Calder, Bridgewater Canal

Fallwood Marina, Pollard Lane, Bramley, Leeds, West Yorks
Tel: (0532) 581074

Suits:	all craft
Availability:	0900-1730 mon-fri, 1000-1600 sat and sun, closed tues
Restrictions:	steep slipway
Facilities:	no fuel, parking for car and trailer(c), refuse and sewage disposal, water, gas, toilets, overnight moorings, boatyard, crane
Licence:	BW licence
Charge:	yes
Directions:	turn off ring road onto A657 Leeds to Bradford road
Link:	River Mersey, River Douglas/Ribble, Aire and Calder, Bridgewater Canal

LLANGOLLEN CANAL   BW (North West Region)

Harriet Hudson, Canal Office, Birch Road, Ellesmere, Shropshire SY12 9AA
Tel: (0691) 622549

One of the most popular cruising canals with its great aqueducts at Chirk and Pontcsyllte, it was originally planned to connect the Mersey to the Severn but is now navigable for 46 miles from Llantisilio to Hurleston Junction where it connects with the Shropshire Union Canal. There is a speed limit of 4mph.

Whixhall Marina, Alders Lane, Whixall, Shropshire
Tel: (0948) 880420/540

Suits:	all craft
Availability:	0900-1630 daily by prior arrangement
Restrictions:	none
Facilities:	diesel, parking for car and trailer, sewage and refuse disposal, water, gas, pump-out, toilets, overnight moorings, chandlery, boatyard
Licence:	BW licence
Charge:	yes
Directions:	phone for directions
Link:	Shropshire Union Canal

Maestermyn Marine Ltd, Ellesmere Road, Whittington, Oswestry, Shropshire
Tel: (0691) 662424

Suits:	small craft
Availability:	during working hours
Restrictions:	none
Facilities:	diesel, petrol (.5 mile), parking for car and trailer, telephone, sewage and refuse disposal, water, gas, pump-out, toilets, overnight moorings, chandlery and boatyard
Licence:	BW licence
Charge:	yes
Directions:	turn off the A5 north-east of Oswestry onto the A495: site is adjacent to road between Whittington and Ellesmere
Link:	Shropshire Union Canal

MACCLESFIELD CANAL   BW (North West Region)

Ian Fullerton, Vesta Street, Ancoats, Manchester M4 6DS
Tel: 061-273 4686

Built as an alternative link between the Midlands and Manchester, the 28 mile long canal links the Peak Forest Canal and the Trent and Mersey Canal. It now forms part of the 100 mile "Cheshire Ring" canal circuit. There is a speed limit of 4mph.

Heritage Narrowboats, The Marina, Kent Green, Stoke-on-Trent, Staffs
Tel: (0782) 785700

Suits:	craft up to 24' LOA
Availability:	0830-1730 daily except sat
Restrictions:	exit from ramp requires tight turn so 4-wheel drive vehicles are best
Facilities:	fuel, parking for car and trailer(c), telephone, sewage and refuse disposal, water, gas, pump-out, boatyard
Licence:	BW licence
Charge:	yes

Directions: leave M6 at exit 16 taking A500 towards Stoke and after three miles take A34 towards Congleton. After two and a half miles cross A50, then after a further one and a quarter miles turn right into Station Road at signpost "Mow Cop": after crossing canal, turn left and marina is 150yds on left

Link: Trent and Mersey and Peak Forest Canals

Macclesfield Boat Co., Swettenham Wharf, Brook Street, Macclesfield, Cheshire
Tel: (0625) 420042

Suits: craft up to 23' LOA and with 2'10" draught and 6'10" beam
Restrictions: none
Facilities: diesel, parking for car and trailer(c), sewage and refuse disposal, water, gas, toilets, overnight moorings, chandlery, boatyard
Licence: BW licence
Charge: yes
Directions: leave M6 at junction 17 taking A534, A54 and A523
Link: Trent and Mersey and Peak Forest Canals

Marineville Moorings, Lyme Road, Higher Poynton, Stockport, Cheshire
Tel: (0625) 876889/871310

Suits: craft up to 25' LOA
Availability: during working hours by prior arrangement
Restrictions: permission to launch must be obtained before crossing canal bridge: slipway has drop at end
Facilities: diesel, water(c), gas; chandlery and boatyard opposite
Licence: BW licence
Charge: yes
Directions: from A523 north of Macclesfield, turn up Park Lane at Poynton traffic lights by the church; after two miles turn left into Shrigley Road North then right into Lyme Road by the Boar's Head: site is by bridge 15
Link: Trent and Mersey and Peak Forest Canals

Lyme View Marina, Adlington Basin, Poynton, Stockport, Cheshire
Tel: (0625) 874638

Suits: craft up to 24' LOA
Availability: daily during working hours
Restrictions: none
Facilities: diesel, parking for car and trailer, sewage and refuse disposal, water, gas, pump-out, toilets, cafe, shop
Licence: BW licence
Charge: yes
Directions: from A523 north of Macclesfield, turn east at Poynton lights into Dickens Lane/Street Lane, then into Woods Lane
Link: Trent and Mersey and Peak Forest Canals

Tonbridge District Office, Medway House, Powder Mill Lane, Leigh, Tonbridge,
Kent TN11 9AS
Tel: (0732) 838858

The River Medway Navigation gives access to 19 miles of the fresh water river above
its tidal limit at Allington Lock and to the tidal river and Thames Estuary below. The
lock is accessible from 3 hours before to 2 hours after HW Tel: (0622) 752864. All
vessels using the navigation must be registered and there is a speed limit of 5 knots.

Allington Marina, Allington, Maidstone, Kent
Tel: (0622) 752057

Suits:	small craft
Availability:	by arrangement
Restrictions:	none
Facilities:	diesel, petrol, parking for car and trailer(c), water, gas, toilets
Licence:	available at Allington Lock Office
Charge:	yes
Directions:	leave M20 at junction 6 following the A229 south and the A20 west: turn right down Castle Road opposite the garage
Link:	tidal river and Thames Estuary via Allington Lock

Record Tennis Centre, St. Peter's Street, Maidstone, Kent
Tel: (0622) 681987

Suits:	small craft
Availability:	by arrangement
Restrictions:	none
Facilities:	fuel, parking for car and trailer(c), water, gas from Allington Marina
Licence:	available at Tennis Centre Office
Charge:	yes
Directions:	turn down St. Peter's Street under the arch at the bottom of the hill
Link:	tidal river and Thames Estuary via Allington Lock

Tovil Bridge Boatyard, Beaconsfield Road, Tovil, Maidstone, Kent
Tel: (0622) 686341

Suits:	craft up to 20' LOA
Availability:	during working hours
Restrictions:	none
Facilities:	diesel, parking for car and trailer, water, boatyard, engine repairs
Licence:	available from Allington Lock or Medway Wharf Marina
Charge:	yes
Directions:	turn off the A26 at Teston onto the B2010 and turn left in Tovil into Church Street and Wharfe Road and right into Beaconsfield Road
Link:	tidal river and Thames Estury via Allington Lock

Medway Wharf Marina, Bow Bridge, Wateringbury, Kent

Tel: (0622) 813927

Suits:	craft up to 32' LOA-also cranage facilities
Availability:	0800-1900 daily
Restrictions:	steep slipway: launching by yard staff if required
Facilities:	fuel (.5 mile), parking for car and trailer(c), telephone, toilets, chandlery and boatyard
Licence:	available from marina
Charge:	yes
Directions:	follow A26 from Maidstone turning left at traffic lights in Wateringbury: turn left half a mile down hill going over bridge and then take first right
Link:	tidal river and Thames Estuary via Allington Lock

Hampstead Slipway, Hampstead Lock, Yalding, Kent

Suits:	craft up to 25' LOA
Availability:	0900-1600 mon-fri; 0900 to 1 hour before sunset sat, sun and Bank Holidays apr-oct
Restrictions:	steep slipway: launch by arrangement with lock-keeper at lifting bridge adjacent Anchor pub, Yalding: access is difficult and parking close by prohibited
Facilities:	fuel and parking (.5 mile), chandlery and boatyard available locally; water, refuse and sewage facilities available at NRA depot
Licence:	NRA licence available on site
Charge:	yes
Directions:	turn off B2015 at Nettlestead Green into Station Road, then on to Hampstead Lane and over the level crossing: site entrance is on left opposite the entrance to the ICI factory
Link:	tidal river and Thames Estuary via Allington Lock

Lower Castle Field, Brightfriars Meadow, Tonbridge, Kent

Suits:	craft up to 20' LOA
Availability:	during daylight hours
Restrictions:	access is via narrow and often congested streets and the car park has a height restriction of 6'
Facilities:	fuel(.5 mile), parking for car and trailer(c), telephone, toilets, sewage and refuse disposal at Town Lock
Licence:	NRA licence available from TIC at Castle
Charge:	no
Directions:	follow A26 into Tonbridge High Street, turning left after the castle into Castle Street and following the Slade to riverside car park
Link:	tidal river and Thames Estuary via Allington Lock

MIDDLE LEVEL NAVIGATIONS   Middle Level Commissioners

Middle Level Offices, Dartford Road, March, Cambs PE15 8AF
Tel: (0354) 53232

This complex system of channels which occupies much of the lowland between the
Rivers Nene and Ouse dates from the mid 17th century. Pleasure craft are not
required to pay a licence fee but visitors should register with the lock-keeper at
Stanground or Salters Lode when entering the system. There is a maximum speed
limit of 5mph with the exception of Kings Dyke and Well Creek, where the limit is
4mph.

C T Fox, 10, Marina Drive, March, Cambs
Tel: (0354) 52770

Suits:	all craft
Availability:	during working hours by arrangement only
Restrictions:	none
Facilities:	fuel, parking for car and trailer(c), water, gas, boatyard
Licence:	none but registration required
Charge:	yes
Directions:	leave the A141 at March roundabout taking Turves exit and bearing left into Marina Drive
Link:	Rivers Nene and Great Ouse

MONMOUTHSHIRE AND BRECON CANAL   BW (South West Region)

Richard Dommett, Canal Office, The Wharf, Govilon, Abergavenny,
Gwent NP7 9NY
Tel: (0873) 830328

The navigable length from Pontypool to Brecon, once the original Brecknock and
Abergavenny Canal has been restored, giving a cruising length of just over 33 miles.

Pontymoile Basin, Pontypool, Gwent

Suits:	all craft
Availability:	key from any BW office
Restrictions:	long lines required if windy
Facilities:	refuse and sewage disposal, water
Licence:	BW licence
Charge:	yes
Directions:	leave M4 at junction 26 taking A4042 north and turning off to Pontypool: site is north of canal bridge 52
Link:	none

Red Line Boats, Goytre Wharf, Llanover, Pontypool, Gwent
Tel: (0873) 880516

Suits:	all craft
Availability:	0900-1800 daily
Restrictions:	none
Facilities:	parking for car and trailer(c), sewage and refuse disposal, water, gas, pump-out, toilets and showers, chandlery, boatyard, engine repairs
Licence:	BW licence
Charge:	yes
Directions:	leave M4 at junction 26 taking A4042 north and turning left at Llanover: contact yard for advice on best route
Link:	none

BW Govilon Yard, Govilon, Gwent
Tel: (0873) 830328

Suits:	craft up to 20'LOA
Availability:	by arrangement only
Restrictions:	none
Facilities:	refuse and sewage disposal, water, toilets
Licence:	BW licence
Charge:	yes
Directions:	leave the A40 at Abergavenny taking the A465 towards Brynmawr, forking left to follow signs to Blaenavon: site is on B4246
Link:	none

MONTGOMERY CANAL   BW (North West Region)

Harriet Hudson, Canal Office, Birch Road, Ellesmere, Shropshire SY12 9AA
Tel: (0691) 622549

This canal was planned to run northwards from Newtown and joined the Llangollen Canal at Frankton Junction. Part of the canal has been restored but there are serious obstacles to complete restoration. Speed limit 4mph.

Pool Quay, Wern, Powys

Suits:	small craft
Availability:	during working hours
Restrictions:	access to approx. eight miles navigable canal: steep gated slipway and approach via narrow road and hump-backed bridge
Facilities:	no fuel, parking for car and trailer
Licence:	purchase a BW sanitary key to gain access
Charge:	yes
Directions:	turn off A483 north of Welshpool and over the old railway crossing: site is below Bugeddin Locks
Links:	none

Smithfield Car Park, Welshpool, Powys

Suits:	small craft only
Availability:	during daylight hours
Restrictions:	site gives access to eight miles navigable canal
Facilities:	parking for car and trailer(c), overnight moorings, sewage disposal
Licence:	purchase BW sanitary key to gain access
Charge:	yes
Directions:	turn off A483 by Spar shop into Church Street: site is in car park

RIVER NENE   NRA (Anglian Region)

Kingfisher House, Goldhay Way, Orton Goldhay, Peterborough PE2 0ZR
Tel: (0733) 371811

The river is tidal for 25 miles as far as the Dog-in-a-Doublet lock and sluice, five miles below Peterborough and is controlled by the Port of Wisbech Authority. The lock is open daily from 0730-sunset: it is advisable to telephone the lock-keeper in advance Tel: (0733) 202219 to make arrangements. Above the lock, the river is navigable to Northampton and thence to the Grand Union Canal via the Northampton Branch. Entry to the Middle Levels and thence the River Ouse and the sea is via Stanground Lock. There is a speed limit of 7mph with a derestricted stretch of water one mile downstream of Peterborough.

Billing Aquadrome Ltd. Crow Lane, Great Billing, Northampton, Northants
Tel: (0604) 408181

Suits:	all craft
Availability:	1000-1700 daily
Restrictions:	none
Facilities:	fuel, parking for car and trailer(c), telephone, sewage and refuse disposal, water, gas, toilets and showers, overnight moorings, chandlery, boatyard, engine repairs
Licence:	NRA licence required
Charge:	no
Directions:	turn off M1 at junction 16, taking the A45 east
Link:	Grand Union Canal, River Ouse, North Sea

Wellingborough Upper Lock, Wellingborough, Northants
Tel: (0536) 517721

Suits:	all trailable craft
Availability:	during daylight hours
Restrictions:	access is difficult with a fairly tight turn
Facilities:	no parking on site, water, toilets (.25 mile)
Licence:	NRA licence required
Charge:	no
Directions:	follow A45 east from Northampton, turning off onto A509: site is downstream of lock and access is via Turnells Mill Lane
Link:	Grand Union Canal, River Ouse, North Sea

Mill Marina, Midland Road, Thrapston, Northants
Tel: (08012) 2850

Suits:	craft up to 20′ LOA or 25′ LOA at high water only
Availability:	0900-2000 or dusk, Easter to end dec
Restrictions:	none
Facilities:	fuel (.5 mile), parking for car and trailer(c), telephone, sewage and refuse disposal, water, gas, toilets and showers, overnight moorings
Licence:	NRA licence
Charge:	yes
Directions:	follow A604 west from Huntingdon, taking A605 south in Thrapston towards Raunds then follow caravan signs
Link:	Grand Union Canal, River Ouse, North Sea

Oundle Marina, Barnwell Road, Oundle, Northants
Tel: (0832) 72762

Suits:	all craft
Availability:	0900-1800 (closed wed) or by arrangement
Restrictions:	none
Facilities:	fuel, parking for car and trailer(c), sewage and refuse disposal, water, gas, toilets, and showers, chandlery, boatyard
Licence:	NRA licence required
Charge:	yes
Directions:	follow A605 from A1 towards Oundle, turning off to right
Link:	Grand Union Canal, River Ouse, North Sea

Yarwell Mill Caravan Park, Yarwell, Peterborough, Cambs
Tel: (0780) 782247

Suits:	trailable craft up to 28′ LOA
Availability:	during daylight hours
Restrictions:	none
Facilities:	parking for car and trailer, toilets and showers, pub nearby
Licence:	NRA licence required
Charge:	yes
Directions:	turn off A1 west of Peterborough at A47 intersection, following signs to Yarwell at Wansford Church
Link:	Grand Union Canal, River Ouse, North Sea

Potters Way, Fengate, Peterborough, Cambs
Tel: (0733) 63141

Suits:	craft up to 20′ LOA
Availability:	during daylight hours
Restrictions:	barrier restricts height to 7′: key to barrier is available from Leisure and Amenities Dept. of City Council Tel: (0733) 63141
Facilities:	parking for car and trailer(c): fuel, chandlery etc. from Peterborough Boating Centre, 73 North Street
Licence:	NRA licence required
Charge:	no

| Directions: | turn into Potters Way in City Centre: access is through car park |
| Link: | Grand Union Canal, River Ouse, North Sea |

Drake Towage, Crab Marsh, Wisbech, Cambs

Tel: (0945) 589539

Suits:	all craft up to 70' LOA
Availability:	from 2 hours before HW to 1 hour after by prior arrangement
Restrictions:	none
Facilities:	fuel, parking for car and trailer, toilets, crane and winch
Licence:	no
Charge:	yes
Directions:	follow A47 to main port area, past ship turning area
Link:	Grand Union Canal, River Ouse, North Sea

GREAT OUSE RIVER   NRA (Anglian Region)

Kingfisher House, Goldhay Way, Orton Goldhay, Peterborough PE2 0ZR
Tel: (0733) 371811

The river is navigable from Bedford to Denver Sluice. The navigation authority for the lower reaches of the river and seaward approaches to King's Lynn is the King's Lynn Conservancy Board. Access to the sea is via Denver Sluice and to the Middle Levels and thence the River Nene via Stanground Sluice. There is a speed limit of 6 knots unless otherwise specified.

Crosshall Marine, Crosshall Road, St. Neots, Cambs

Tel: (0480) 472763

Suits:	small craft only
Availability:	0900-1930 daily in summer: closed in winter
Restrictions:	access restricts width to 7'
Facilities:	diesel, water, gas, toilets and showers, overnight moorings, chandlery, boatyard
Licence:	NRA licence
Charge:	yes
Directions:	follow signs to Golf Club: access is through club car park
Link:	North Sea, Middle Levels, River Nene

Buckden Marina, Buckden, Nr. Huntingdon, Cambs

Tel: (0480) 810355

Suits:	all craft
Availability:	0800-1800 daily
Restrictions:	none
Facilities:	fuel, parking for car and trailer(c), refuse and sewage disposal, water, gas, toilets, overnight moorings, chandlery, boatyard with crane, engine repairs
Licence:	NRA licence required
Charge:	yes

Directions:	turn east off A1 south of Huntingdon, to Buckden: site is below Offord Lock
Link:	North Sea, Middle Levels, River Nene

Hartford Road Car Park, Huntingdon, Cambs

Suits:	craft up to 20' LOA
Availability:	during daylight hours
Restrictions:	sharp drop at end of slipway
Facilities:	fuel (.5 mile), parking for car and trailer
Licence:	NRA licence required
Charge:	no
Directions:	follow ring road round town, turning off to follow signs to St. Ives: after 50yds, cross over into car park by river; site is downstream of Purvis Marine
Link:	North Sea, Middle Levels, River Nene

Hartford Marina, Banks End, Wyton, Huntingdon, Cambs
Tel: (0480) 454677/8

Suits:	craft up to 60' LOA and with 3' draught
Availability:	0800-1700 daily
Restrictions:	none
Facilities:	fuel, parking for car and trailer(c), telephone, refuse and sewage disposal, water, gas, toilets and showers, chandlery, boatyard with crane, engine repairs, restaurant and caravan site
Licence:	NRA licence required
Charge:	yes
Directions:	turn off A1123 between Huntingdon and St. Ives
Link:	North Sea, Middle Levels, River Nene

Town Quay, St. Ives, Cambs

Suits:	small craft only
Availability:	during daylight hours
Restrictions:	none
Facilities:	fuel nearby, parking for car and trailer(c), toilets, chandlery from The Boathaven
Licence:	NRA licence required
Charge:	none
Directions:	turn off eastern bypass road at the Meadow Lane junction; site is at the quay downstream of the old bridge
Link:	North Sea, Middle Levels, River Nene

The Boathaven, Low Road, St. Ives, Cambs
Tel: (0480) 494040

Suits:	all craft
Availability:	daily during normal working hours
Restrictions:	none
Facilities:	fuel, parking for car and trailer(c), telephone, refuse and sewage disposal, water, gas, toilets and showers, overnight moorings, chandlery, boatyard, engine repairs
Licence:	NRA licence required
Charge:	turn off the A1096 bypass at roundabout south of St. Ives into Low Road following signs to Fenstanton, then turn off to marina
Link:	North Sea, Middle Levels, River Nene

West View Marina, High Street, Earith, Cambs
Tel: (0487) 841627

Suits:	larger craft: launching by crane only
Availability:	0900-1700 daily by prior arrangement only
Restrictions:	no slipway
Facilities:	diesel, parking for car and trailer(c) by arrangement, refuse disposal, water, gas, toilets and showers, overnight moorings, engine repairs
Licence:	NRA licence required
Charge:	yes
Directions:	follow the A1123 east from Huntingdon to Earith
Link:	North Sea, Middle Levels, River Nene

Hermitage Marina, Earith, Cambs
Tel: (0487) 840994

Suits:	all craft
Availability:	0830-1800 daily in summer, 0900-1800 daily in winter
Restrictions:	none
Facilities:	fuel, parking for car and trailer(c), sewage and refuse disposal, water, gas, toilets, overnight moorings, chandlery, engine repairs
Licence:	NRA licence required
Charge:	yes
Directions:	follow the A1123 east from Huntingdon to Earith
Link:	North Sea, Middle Levels, River Nene

Bridge Boatyard, Bridge Road, Ely, Cambs
Tel: (0353) 663726

Suits:	craft up to 32' LOA
Availability:	during daylight hours
Restrictions:	steep slipway
Facilities:	parking for car and trailer(c), refuse disposal, water, gas, toilets, boatyard, tractor assistance if required, engine repairs
Licence:	NRA licence required
Charge:	yes

Directions: in Ely take the A142 towards Newmarket: site is near railway station
Link: North Sea, Middle Levels, River Nene

Ely Marina, Waterside, Ely Cambs

Te: (0353) 664622

Suits: craft up to 20' LOA
Availability: 0900-1800 daily
Restrictions: none
Facilities: fuel, parking for car and trailer(c), telephone, refuse and sewage dis-
              posal, water, gas, toilets and showers, overnight moorings, chandlery,
              boatyard with crane, engine repairs
Licence: NRA licence required
Charge: yes
Directions: follow the A10 from Cambridge into Ely, then follow signs to river
Link: North Sea, Middle Levels, River Nene

Waterside, Ely, Cambs

Suits: small craft only
Availability: during daylight hours
Restrictions: launching over shingle only
Facilities: fuel, parking for car and trailer, other facilities at Ely marina nearby
Licence: NRA licence required
Charge: yes
Directions: from A142 turn into Broad Street and follow signs to river
Link: North Sea, Middle Levels, River Nene

Denver Sluice, Denver, Norfolk

Tel: (0366) 382340

Suits: small craft
Availability: during daylight hours
Restrictions: tidal limit of river: obtain key from lock-keeper
Facilities: no fuel, parking for car and trailer, pub adjacent
Licence: NRA licence required
Charge: yes
Directions: follow A10 north towards Downham Market, taking the B1507 to
              Denver and following signs to Sluice: site is adjacent to Jenyns Arms
Link: North Sea, Middle Levels, River Nene

RIVER OUSE (YORKSHIRE)   BW (North East Region)

Keith Boswell, Naburn Locks, Naburn, Yorks YO1 4RU
Tel: (0904) 87229

The river is tidal for 30 miles from Goole to Naburn Lock and commercial traffic still
reaches York, six miles further on. It is advisable to contact the lock-keeper at Naburn
the day before you wish to go through the lock Tel: (0904) 87229. There is a speed
limit of 5 knots in force through York from Clifton Bridge to York Motor Club premises

at Fulford: elsewhere it is 6 knots. The river above Linton Lock comes under the juris-diction of the Linton Lock Commissioners, 1-3 Wheelgate, Malton, North Yorks YO17 OHT.

Tower Marine Services, Boroughbridge Marina, Roecliffe Lane, Boroughbridge, Yorks
Tel: (0423) 322011

Suits:	craft up to 40' LOA 13' beam and 5' draught
Availability:	0900-2200 daily
Restrictions:	none
Facilities:	fuel, parking for car and trailer(c), toilets, chandlery and boatyard
Licence:	BW licence available on site
Charge:	yes
Directions:	from the A1 turn onto the B6265 to Boroughbridge
Link:	River Ure, Ripon Canal, River Humber, North Sea

Waterline Leisure, Waterline Estate, Acaster Malbis, York
Tel: (0904) 702049

Suits:	slipway with winch and rollers suitable for craft up to 30' LOA
Availability:	during daylight hours by prior arrangement
Restrictions:	none
Facilities:	fuel nearby, parking for car and trailer, toilets, cafe
Licence:	BW licence required
Charge:	yes
Directions:	turn off A64 Leeds to York road at Copmanthorpe onto A1036: turn left in Bishopthorpe, then right to Acaster Malbis
Link:	River Ure, Ripon Canal, River Humber, North Sea

York Marine Services Ltd, Ferry Lane, Bishopthorpe, North Yorks
Tel: (0904) 704442

Suits:	craft up to 27' LOA
Availability:	0830-1800 daily
Restrictions:	all slipping and recovery of craft is carried out by yard staff using tractor but dinghies may be launched by hand for a small charge
Facilities:	fuel, parking for car and trailer(c), toilets, telephone, chandlery and boatyard
Licence:	BW licence required
Charge:	yes
Directions:	from A64 York bypass exit on A1036 signposted to Bishopthorpe village: turn left at "T" junction in village main street, turning right into Acaster Lane for Acaster Malbis and turning left after 150 yds
Link:	River Ure, Ripon Canal, River Humber, North Sea

Ian Mormont, The Doles, Priors Marston, Rugby, Warwicks CV23 8SS
Tel: (0926) 812882

One of the earliest canals in southern England, it was built to facilitate the transport
of coal from the Warwickshire coalfield to Banbury and Oxford and thence the
Thames. Now a very popular cruising waterway it runs for 77 miles from the junction
with the Coventry Canal (Hawkesbury Junction) to Oxford where it joins the Thames.
There are connections with the Grand Union Canal at Napton and Braunston
Junctions.

Cowroast Ltd, Fenny Marina, Station Fields, Fenny Compton, Warwicks
Tel: (0295) 770461/2

Suits:	all craft
Availability:	0900-1730 daily by prior arrangement
Restrictions:	none
Facilities:	diesel, parking for car and trailer(c), sewage and refuse disposal, water, gas, pump-out, overnight moorings, chandlery and boatyard
Licence:	BW licence required
Charge:	yes
Directions:	follow A423 north from Banbury for eight miles, turning left after crossing the canal at bridge 136
Link:	River Thames, Coventry Canal, Grand Union Canal

Napton Narrowboats, Napton Marina, Napton on the Hill, Stockton, Warwicks
Tel: (092 681) 3644

Suits:	all craft
Availability:	0900-1730 daily by prior arrangement
Restrictions:	none
Facilities:	diesel, parking for car and trailer(c), sewage and refuse disposal, water, pump-out, toilets, overnight moorings, chandlery, boatyard
Licence:	BW licence required
Charge:	yes
Directions:	follow A423 north from Banbury turning onto A425 at Southam and following signs: site is 300 yds south of the junction of the Oxford and Grand Union Canals
Link:	River Thames, Coventry Canal, Grand Union Canal

Rose Narrowboats Ltd, Stretton-under-Fosse, Rugby, Warwicks
Tel: (0788) 832449

Suits:	craft up to 27' LOA and 7' wide
Availability:	during working hours by arrangement only
Restrictions:	access is restricted as slipway is on other side of canal and boats have to be transported across the canal before launching
Facilities:	fuel, parking for car and trailer(c), sewage and refuse disposal, water, gas, pump-out, overnight moorings, chandlery, boatyard
Licence:	BW licence

Charge:	yes
Directions:	follow the A427 Fosse Way one mile north of Brinklow
Link:	River Thames, Coventry Canal, Grand Union Canal

PEAK FOREST CANAL

BW (North West Region)

Ian Fullerton, Vesta Street, Ancoats, Manchester M4 6DS
Tel: 061-273 4686

This canal runs from the Ashton Canal at Ashton for 14 miles to Whaley Bridge and connects with the Macclesfield Canal at Marple Junction.

New Mills Marina, Hibbert Street, New Mills, Derbs
Tel: (0663) 745000

Suits:	all craft
Availability:	0900-1800 daily by prior arrangement: assisted launch available
Restrictions:	none
Facilities:	diesel, parking for car and trailer(c), sewage and refuse disposal, water, gas, toilets, overnight moorings, chandlery and boatyard
Licence:	BW licence
Charge:	yes
Directions:	from central Manchester follow the A6 south to New Mills: site is seven miles south east of Stockport
Link:	Ashton Canal, Macclesfield Canal

ROCHDALE CANAL

Rochdale Canal Trust

Rochdale Canal Workshops, Callis Mill, Charlestown, Hebden Bridge West Yorks
Tel: (0422) 844990

The canal was originally built as a 33 mile link over the Pennines between the Mersey and the rivers of Yorkshire. It is now navigable from Sowerby Bridge to Littleborough and connection to the Calder and Hebble at Sowerby Bridge is planned for Spring 1995.

Hebden Bridge Marina, New Road, Hebden Bridge, West Yorks
Tel: (0422) 844990

Suits:	craft up to 12' wide
Availability:	during daylight hours
Restrictions:	by arrangement with Canal Trust: access is controlled
Facilities:	fuel (.25 mile) parking for car and trailer nearby
Licence:	from Rochdale Canal Trust
Charge:	no
Directions:	follow A646 west from Halifax to town centre
Link:	none

Kwiksave Car Park, Sowerby Bridge, West Yorks
Tel: (0422) 844990 (Canal Trust)

Suits:	all craft
Availability:	during daylight hours
Restrictions:	by arrangement with Canal Trust
Facilities:	fuel (100yds), parking for car and trailer adjacent, telephone (100yds), toilets, chandlery from Sowerby Marine, boatyard from Shire Cruisers
Licence:	from Rochdale Canal Trust
Charge:	yes
Directions:	turn off the A58 Wharf Street in town centre into the car park
Link:	none

RIVER SEVERN   BW (South West Region)

Andrew Stumpf, Llanthony Warehouse, Gloucester Docks, Gloucester Gl1 2EH
Tel: (0452) 525524

One of the most important navigations in the country, linking the Midlands and Wales to the Bristol Channel and thence the open sea, a canal was built in the 19th century from Sharpness to Gloucester to improve its viability. There are connections with the River Avon at Tewkesbury, the Worcester and Birmingham Canal at Diglis Junction and the Staffs and Worcs Canal at Stourport. There is a speed limit of 6mph above Kempsey and 8mph below.

Lower Lode Hotel, Forthampton, Tewkesbury, Glos
Tel: (0684) 293224

Suits:	craft up to 30' LOA
Availability:	during daylight hours
Restrictions:	access is via a narrow lane: get permission to launch from hotel
Facilities:	fuel (3 miles), parking for car and trailer(c), telephone, toilets, overnight moorings, bar meals
Licence:	BW licence
Charge:	yes
Directions:	follow A438 Tewkesbury to Ledbury road turning into Forthampton village and follow signs to Lower Lode: site is disused ferry slipway
Link:	Bristol Channel, River Avon; Worcs and Birmingham and Staffs and Worcs Canals

Upton Marina, Upton-on-Severn, Worcs
Tel: (068459) 311

Suits:	all craft
Availability:	during daylight working hours
Restrictions:	steep slipway levels off into shallow water
Facilities:	fuel, parking for car and trailer, telephone, sewage and refuse disposal, water, gas, pump-out, toilets and showers, overnight moorings, chandlery, boatyard, engine repairs
Licence:	BW licence

Charge:	yes
Directions:	follow the A38 north from Gloucester, turning onto the A4104 north of Tewkesbury
Link:	Bristol Channel, River Avon; Worcs and Birmingham and Staffs and Worcs Canals

SHEFFIELD AND SOUTH YORKS NAVIGATION
BW (North East Region)

John Nuttall, Dun Street, Swinton, Mexborough, South Yorks S64 8AR
Tel: (0709) 582770

Comprising four different waterways, this navigation connects Sheffield with the sea via the New Junction Canal, which was the last canal to be built in the country. There are connections with the Aire and Calder Navigation and the Stainforth and Keadby Canal and thence the River Trent. Speed limit 4mph.

Sheffield Canal Co Ltd, Sussex Street Wharf, Sheffield, South Yorks
Tel: (0742) 727233

Suits:	all craft
Availability:	during working hours except by special arrangement
Restrictions:	canal basin development programme in progress: please phone yard to ensure availability of facility
Facilities:	fuel, parking for car and trailer(c), telephone, refuse and sewage disposal, water, gas, pump-out, toilets, chandlery and boatyard
Licence:	BW licence
Charge:	yes
Directions:	from A61, Victoria Station approach junction, turn along Furnival Road, then take second right into Sussex Street: access to site is after 200 yds on right
Link:	Aire and Calder Navigation, Stainforth and Keadby Canal, River Trent

Tulleys Marine Services, Canal Wharf, Sheffield, South Yorks
Tel: (0742) 731717

Suits:	all craft
Availability:	1000-1630 tues-sun: closed mon
Restrictions:	headroom restricted to 13'1"
Facilities:	diesel on site, petrol (.25 mile), parking for car and trailer, telephone, toilets nearby, chandlery and boatyard, 16 ton boat hoist
Licence:	BW licence
Charge:	yes
Directions:	turn left off the southbound carriageway of Sheaf Street just before Parkway interchange: site is opposite Sheffield's Sheaf Market
Link:	Aire and Calder Navigation, Stainforth and Keadby Canal, River Trent

Ellesmere Port to Audlem and Middlewich – Peter Bentham, Lighterage Yard, Chesterway, Northwich, Cheshire CW9 5JT
Tel:(0606) 40566

Audlem to Autherley - David Green, Norbury Junction, Norbury, Stafford ST20 OPN
Tel: (0785) 284253

The canal connects with the Staffordshire and Worcester Canal at Autherley Junction and the Llangollen Canal at Hurleston Junction before finally meeting the Manchester Ship Canal at Ellesmere Port. The Middlewich Branch of the canal connects the Shropshire Union to the Trent and Mersey Canal. There is a speed limit of 4mph.

Water Travel, Autherley Junction, Oxley Moor Road, Wolverhampton, West Midlands

Tel: (0902) 782371

Suits:	all craft
Availability:	0800-1500 daily
Restrictions:	steep slipway
Facilities:	diesel, parking for car and trailer, telephone, sewage and refuse disposal, water, gas, pump-out, toilets, overnight moorings, chandlery, boatyard, engine repairs
Licence:	BW licence required
Charge:	yes
Directions:	phone for directions
Link:	Staffs and Worcs Canal, Llangollen Canal, Trent and Mersey Canal

Countryside Cruisers, The Wharf, Brewood, Staffs

Tel: (0902) 850166

Suits:	all craft
Availability:	0900-1700 daily
Restrictions:	none
Facilities:	fuel, parking for car and trailer(c), telephone, sewage and refuse disposal, water, gas, pump-out, toilet, boatyard, engine repairs
Licence:	BW licence required
Charge:	yes
Directions:	leave M6 at junction 12 taking A5 west, turning off to Brewood: in village turn right towards Bishop's Wood going over canal bridge and turning right immediately: site is 500yds down lane
Link:	Staffs and Worcs Canal, Llangollen Canal, Trent and Mersey Canal

Dartline Cruisers, The Wharf, Norbury Junction, Stafford, Staffs
Tel: (078 574) 292

Suits:	all craft
Availability:	0900-1700 daily
Restrictions:	access is via narrow bridge
Facilities:	diesel, parking for car and trailer(c), telephone, water, gas, pump-out, toilets, overnight moorings, chandlery, boatyard, engine repairs
Licence:	BW licence required
Charge:	yes
Directions:	from the north, leave M6 at exit 15 to Eccleshall and take the A519 towards Newport. One mile after Woodseaves, turn left to Norbury: from the south, leave M6 at exit 13 to Stafford town centre and take the A518 for Newport, turning right at Gnosall for Norbury
Link:	Staffs and Worcs Canal, Llangollen Canal, Trent and Mersey Canal

Barbridge Marina, Wardle, Nantwich, Cheshire
Tel: 027-073 682

Suits:	small craft
Availability:	0900-1800 daily
Restrictions:	steep slipway and narrow bridge limits width of boat to 6'10"
Facilities:	fuel (4 miles), parking for car and trailer(c), telephone, sewage and refuse disposal, water, gas, toilets, overnight moorings
Licence:	BW licence required
Charge:	yes
Directions:	turn off A51 about four miles north of Nantwich
Link:	Staffs and Worcs Canal, Llangollen Canal, Trent and Mersey Canal

BW Chester Yard, Tower Wharf, Chester, Cheshire
Tel: (0244) 390372

Suits:	all craft
Availability:	by prior arrangement only
Restrictions:	none
Facilities:	no fuel, parking for cars only, toilets, refuse disposal, water, dry dock
Licence:	BW licence required
Charge:	yes
Directions:	access is from Raymond Street
Link:	Staffs and Worcs Canal, Llangollen Canal, Trent and Mersey Canal

Venetian Marina Village, Cholmondeston Lock, Nr. Nantwich, Cheshire
Tel: 027-073 251

Suits:	all craft
Availability:	0900-1730 daily by prior arrangement
Restrictions:	none
Facilities:	diesel, parking for car and trailer(c), sewage and refuse disposal, water, gas, toilets, overnight moorings, chandlery, tearoom
Licence:	BW licence required
Charge:	yes

Directions: leave M6 at junction 17 taking A534 to Nantwich then A51 north
Link: Staffs and Worcs Canal, Llangollen Canal, Trent and Mersey Canal

STAINFORTH AND KEADBY CANAL BW (North East Region)

John Nuttall, Dun Street, Swinton, Mexborough, South Yorks S64 8AR
Tel: (0709) 582770

This canal connects the Sheffield and South Yorks Navigation at Bramwith Lock with the River Trent at Keadby

Staniland Marina, Lock Lane, Thorne, South Yorks
Tel: (0405) 813150

Suits: all craft
Availability: during working hours 0800-1630 daily
Restrictions: none
Facilities: parking for car and trailer, refuse disposal, water, gas, toilets, overnight moorings, chandlery, boatyard
Licence: BW licence required
Charge: yes
Directions: leave M18 at junction 6 following signs to Thorne
Link: Sheffield and South Yorks Navigation, River Trent

Blue Water Marina, Thorne, South Yorks
Tel: (0405) 813165

Suits: small craft
Availability: 0800-1700 daily
Restrictions: none
Facilities: diesel, parking for car and trailer(c), sewage and refuse disposal, water, gas, pump-out, toilets and showers, overnight moorings, chandlery, boatyard, clubhouse
Licence: BW licence required
Charge: yes
Directions: turn off M18 at junction 6: site is opposite South Station, Thorne
Link: Sheffield and South Yorks Navigations, River Trent

STAFFORDSHIRE AND WORCESTERSHIRE CANAL
BW (Midlands Region)

Stourport to Gailey - David Green, Norbury Junction, Norbury, Stafford ST290 OPN Tel: (0785) 284253

Gailey to Gt. Haywood - Stephen Goode, Fradley Junction, Alrewas, Burton-on-Trent, Staffs DE13 7DN
Tel: (0283) 790236

This canal joins the River Severn at Stourport and the Trent and Mersey Canal at Great Haywood Junction and runs a distance of 46 miles; there are also connections with the Birmingham Canal at Aldersley Junction and the Shropshire Union Canal at Autherley Junction. It is now a delightful canal for cruising. There is a speed limit of 4mph.

Severn Valley Cruisers, York Street Boatyard, Stourport-on-Severn, Worcs
Tel: (02993) 71165

Suits:	all craft
Availability:	during working hours by prior arrangement
Restrictions:	none
Facilities:	diesel, petrol (.25 mile), parking for car and trailer(c) nearby, sewage and refuse disposal, water, gas, pump-out, toilets, overnight moorings, chandlery and boatyard with crane, engine repairs
Directions:	site is off York Street: turn left immediately after crossing the canal
Link:	River Severn; Trent and Mersey, Birmingham and Shropshire Union Canals

Ashwood Marina, Kingswinford, West Midlands
Tel: (0384) 295535

Suits:	trailable canal craft
Availability:	0900-1700 daily
Restrictions:	fairly steep slipway with winch
Facilities:	diesel, petrol (1 mile), parking for car and trailer(c), sewage and refuse disposal, water, gas, toilets and showers, overnight moorings, chandlery and boatyard, engine repairs, restaurant
Licence:	BW licence available on site
Charge:	yes
Directions:	turn off the A449 at Kingswinford into Doctors Lane
Link:	River Severn; Trent and Mersey, Birmingham and Shropshire Union Canals

Double Pennant Boatyard, Hordern Road, Wolverhampton, West Midlands
Tel: (0902) 752771

Suits:	boats up to 25' LOA, 6'10" wide and 2.5' draught
Availability:	daily 1000-1800 with 24 hours notice
Restrictions:	steep slipway: launching by prior arrangement only
Facilities:	parking for car and trailer(c), water, gas, toilets, chandlery, boatyard
Licence:	BW licence required
Charge:	yes
Directions:	site is close A41 on west side of Wolverhampton
Link:	River Severn; Trent and Mersey, Birmingham and Shropshire Union Canals

Teddesley Boat Company, Park Gate Lock, Teddesley Road, Penkridge, Staffs

Tel: 078-571 4692

Suits:	canal craft
Availability:	during working hours by arrangement
Restrictions:	launching by 32 ton crane only: no slipway
Facilities:	parking for car, sewage and refuse disposal, water, pump-out, toilets, boatyard, engine repairs
Licence:	BW licence required
Charge:	yes
Directions:	turn off A449 north of Penkridge: site is by bridge 90
Link:	River Severn, Trent and Mersey, Birmingham and Shropshire Union Canals

STRATFORD-ON-AVON CANAL   BW (Midlands Region)

Tom Brock, White House, Canal Lane, Hatton, Warwicks CV35 7JL
Tel: (0926) 492192

Built to connect Stratford-on-Avon to the expanding canal network, it meets the Worcs and Birmingham Canal at Kings Norton, the Grand Union at Kingswood Junction and joins the River Avon in Stratford itself. There is a speed limit of 4 mph.

Lyons Boatyard, Canal Side, Limekiln Lane, Warstock, West Midlands

Tel: 021-474 4977

Suits:	all craft
Availability:	during daylight hours by arrangement
Restrictions:	launching by crane only
Facilities:	diesel, petrol (200 yds), parking for car and trailer by arrangement(c), sewage disposal, water, gas, pump-out, toilets and showers, overnight moorings, limited chandlery, boatyard, engine repairs
Licence:	BW licence required
Charge:	yes
Directions:	access via Alcester Road South (A435): site is at bridge 3
Link:	Worcs and Birmingham and Grand Union Canals; River Avon

Earlswood Marine Services, Lady Lane, Earlswood, Warwicks

Tel: (05646) 2552

Suits:	small cabin cruisers only
Availability:	by prior arrangement only
Restrictions:	none
Facilities:	parking for car and trailer(c), sewage and refuse disposal, water, toilets, overnight moorings, dry dock, clubhouse
Licence:	BW licence required
Charge:	yes
Directions:	follow A3400 north from Stratford-on-Avon turning left onto B4102 and into Lady Lane after two miles
Link:	Worcs and Birmingham and Grand Union Canals; River Avon

Swallow Cruisers, Wharf Lane, Hockley Heath, Solihull
Tel: (0564) 783442

Suits:	canal cruisers up to 30' LOA
Availability:	0900-1800 daily: other times by arrangement
Restrictions:	none
Facilities:	diesel, petrol (.5 mile), parking for car and trailer(c), sewage and refuse disposal, water, gas, pump-out, toilets, chandlery and boatyard
Licence:	BW licence requireed
Charge:	yes
Directions:	turn right off the A3400 south of Hockley Heath
Link:	Worcs and Birmingham and Grand Union Canals; River Avon

RIVER THAMES

NON-TIDAL; TEDDINGTON TO CRICKLADE   NRA (Thames Region)
Kings Meadow House, Kings Meadow Road, Reading, Berks RG1 8DQ
Tel: (0734) 535000

The river runs for 215 miles from its source beyond Cricklade to the Thames Estuary. By the end of the 19th century it was linked to the main canal network giving access to many other parts of the country. All boats using the non-tidal river must be registered with and licensed by the NRA.

District 1: St. John's to Benson-Navigation Inspector (0734) 721271

Riverside Lechlade, Parkend Wharf, Lechlade, Glos
Tel: (0367) 252229

Suits:	small craft
Availability:	during daylight hours with permission
Restrictions:	none
Facilities:	fuel, parking for car and trailer(c), telephone, water, gas, toilet, overnight moorings, chandlery, boatyard, engine repairs, pub
Licence:	NRA licence
Charge:	yes
Directions:	follow A361 to Lechlade town centre turning down to Riverside
Link:	Oxford Canal, Kennet and Avon, River Wey, Grand Union Canal

Swan Inn, Radcot Bridge, Radcot, Oxon

Suits:	small craft
Availability:	during daylight hours
Restrictions:	launching with permission from Inn only
Facilities:	limited parking, pub, overnight moorings
Licence:	NRA licence
Charge:	no
Directions:	follow A4095 north from Faringdon and over bridge
Link:	Oxford Canal, Kennet and Avon, River Wey, Grand Union Canal

Suits:	small craft can be launched from disused ferry slipway on either bank
Availability:	during daylight hours
Restrictions:	none
Facilities:	none
Licence:	NRA licence
Charge:	no
Directions:	for west bank, follow B4449 from Stanton Harcourt through West End to river; for east bank, turn off B4017 by post office in Cumnor and follow road to river
Link:	Oxford Canal, Kennet and Avon, River Wey, Grand Union Canal, Lee and Stort, North Sea

Oxford Cruisers, Eynsham, Witney, Oxon
Tel: (0865) 881698

Suits:	all trailable craft
Availability:	0830-1800 mon-thur and sun (fri and sat are very busy days: launching then by prior arrangement only)
Restrictions:	Swinford toll bridge is fairly narrow: drivers towing large craft may need to find an alternative route
Facilities:	fuel, parking for car and trailer(c), telephone, refuse and sewage disposal, water, gas, pump-out, toilets and showers, overnight moorings, boatyard with 5 ton boat lift, engine repairs
Licence:	NRA licence
Charge:	yes
Directions:	take the A40 towards Cheltenham turning left at Jet station roundabout for Eynsham: go through town and over Swinford toll bridge on B4044 turning right after half a mile opposite Stroud Copse
Link:	Oxford Canal, Kennet and Avon, River Wey, Grand Union Canal

Bossoms Boatyard Ltd, Medley, Via Binsey Lane, Oxford, Oxon
Tel: (0865) 247780

Suits:	all craft
Availability:	during working hours only mon-fri and sat am
Restrictions:	closed sat pm and sun
Facilities:	no fuel, parking for car and trailer(c), telephone, water, toilets, overnight moorings, chandlery and boatyard with 4 ton gantry
Licence:	NRA licence
Charge:	yes
Directions:	take A420 Botley Road into Oxford turning left into Binsey Lane and then right to yard
Link:	Oxford Canal, Kennet and Avon, River Wey, Grand Union Canal

Donnington Bridge, via Meadow Lane, Oxford, Oxon

Suits:	small craft
Availability:	during daylight hours
Restrictions:	none
Facilities:	limited parking on site, boatyard nearby
Licence:	NRA licence
Charge:	no
Directions:	site is upstream of bridge on east bank
Link:	Oxford Canal, Kennet and Avon, River Wey, Grand Union Canal

Abingdon Boat Centre, The Bridge, Abingdon, Oxon

Tel: (0235) 521125

Suits:	small craft
Availability:	during working hours only
Restrictions:	none
Facilities:	fuel, parking for car and trailer(c), water, gas, pump-out, chandlery
Licence:	NRA licence
Charge:	yes
Directions:	follow A415 to Abingdon: site is by bridge and opposite the Nags Head pub
Link:	Oxford Canal, Kennet and Avon, River Wey, Grand Union Canal

St. Helen's Wharf, East Street, Abingdon, Oxon

Suits:	small craft only
Availability:	during daylight hours
Restrictions:	access is via narrow one-way street and slipway is steep
Facilities:	fuel (2 miles), no parking, pub opposite
Licence:	NRA licence
Charge:	no
Directions:	follow A415 through Abingdon town centre, turning off to the river: site is near St.Helen's church and opposite the Old Anchor Pub
Link:	Oxford Canal, Kennet and Avon, River Wey, Grand Union Canal

The Lees, Clifton Hampden, Oxon

Suits:	small craft only
Availability:	during daylight hours
Restrictions:	none
Facilities:	no fuel, parking for car and trailer(c), pub nearby
Licence:	NRA licence
Charge:	yes
Directions:	follow A415 into Clifton Hampden turning off to cross the bridge: site is on east bank of river upstream of the bridge and near the Barley Mow Inn
Link:	Oxford Canal, Kennet and Avon, River Wey, Grand Union Canal, Lee and Stort, North Sea

Benson Cruiser Station, Benson, Oxon
Tel: (0491) 38304

Suits:	all craft
Availability:	0830-1730 daily
Restrictions:	none
Facilities:	fuel, parking for car and trailer(c), telephone, sewage and refuse disposal, water, gas, pump-out, toilets and showers, overnight moorings, boatyard, launderette, restaurant
Licence:	NRA licence
Charge:	yes
Directions:	site is on A423 Henley to Oxford road near the junction with the B4009, just upriver of Benson Lock on the east bank
Link:	Oxford Canal, Kennet and Avon, River Wey, Grand Union Canal, Lee and Stort, North Sea

District 2: Cleeve to Hurley-Navigation
Inspector (0734) 535533

Papist Way, Cholsey, Nr. Wallingford, Oxon

Suits:	small craft only
Availability:	during daylight hours
Restrictions:	none
Facilities:	parking, pub nearby
Licence:	NRA licence
Charge:	no
Directions:	turn off A329 south of Wallingford by Fair Mile Hospital
Link:	Oxford Canal, Kennet and Avon, River Wey, Grand Union Canal

Sheridan Uk Marine, Moulsford, Oxon
Tel: (0491) 652085

Suits:	all craft
Availability:	during working hours by prior arrangement: closed winter week-ends
Restrictions:	assisted launch only: access limited by small bridge
Facilities:	petrol, parking for car and trailer(c), water, gas, chandlery, boatyard
Charge:	yes
Directions:	site is off A329 south of Wallingford on the west bank and just downstream of Moulsford Railway Bridge
Link:	Oxford Canal, Kennet and Avon, River Wey, Grand Union Canal

Beetle and Wedge Hotel, Moulsford, Oxon
Tel: (0491) 651381

Suits:	small craft only
Availability:	during daylight hours by prior arrangement only
Restrictions:	none
Facilities:	hotel adjacent offers food and accommodation, overnight moorings
Licence:	NRA licence

Charge:	no
Directions:	follow A329 south from Wallingford, turning down to the river in Moulsford: site is at old ferry crossing beside the hotel
Link:	Oxford Canal, Kennet and Avon, River Wey, Grand Union Canal

Swan Hotel, Pangbourne, Oxon

Tel: (0734) 843199

Suits:	small craft
Availability:	during daylight hours
Restrictions:	launch with permission of the hotel only
Facilities:	hotel adjacent
Licence:	NRA licence
Directions:	follow A329 west from Reading to Pangbourne: site is on south bank of river just upstream of Whitchurch Lock
Link:	Oxford Canal, Kennet and Avon, River Wey, Grand Union Canal

Mapledurham Lock, Purley, Oxon

Suits:	small craft only
Availability:	during daylight hours
Restrictions:	access is over railway bridge
Facilities:	refuse disposal, overnight moorings
Licence:	NRA licence
Charge:	no
Directions:	follow A329 west of Reading into Purley turning off to cross over the railway line and into Mapledurham Drive: site is upriver of the lock
Link:	Oxford Canal, Kennet and Avon, River Wey, Grand Union Canal

Caversham Bridge, Reading, Berks

Suits:	small craft
Availability:	during daylight hours
Restrictions:	none
Facilities:	available locally
Licence:	NRA licence
Charge:	no
Directions:	follow A4155: site is immediately upstream of bridge on south bank
Link:	Oxford Canal, Kennet and Avon, River Wey, Grand Union Canal

Ferry Lane, Wargrave, Berks

Suits:	small craft
Availability:	during daylight hours
Restrictions:	none
Facilities:	in village: pub nearby
Licence:	NRA licence
Charge:	no
Directions:	turn into Ferry Lane from the High Street by the Greyhound pub
Link:	Oxford Canal, Kennet and Avon, River Wey, Grand Union Canal

Hobbs and Sons Ltd, Wargrave Road, Henley-on-Thames, Oxon

Tel: (0491) 572035

Suits:	craft up to 25' LOA 8' beam and 1'6" draught
Availability:	during daylight hours
Restrictions:	none
Facilities:	fuel, parking for car and trailer(c), water, toilets
Licence:	NRA licence
Charge:	yes
Directions:	site is half a mile outside Henley on the Henley to Wargrave road
Link:	Oxford Canal, Kennet and Avon, River Wey, Grand Union Canal

Wharf Lane, Henley-on-Thames, Oxon

Suits:	small craft
Availability:	during daylight hours
Restrictions:	none
Facilities:	available locally
Licence:	NRA licence
Charge:	no
Directions:	cross over Henley Bridge on A432 and turn right: launch at end of Wharf Lane, downstream of the bridge on the west bank
Link:	Oxford Canal, Kennet and Avon, River Wey, Grand Union Canal

Aston Ferry, Hambleden, Bucks

Suits:	small craft
Availability:	during daylight hours
Restrictions:	none
Facilities:	none
Licence:	NRA licence
Charge:	no
Directions:	follow signs from A423 for south bank or A4155 for north bank: launch from either bank at disused ferry slipways
Link:	Oxford Canal, Kennet and Avon, River Wey, Grand Union Canal

Medmenham, Bucks

Suits:	small craft
Availability:	during daylight hours
Restrictions:	none
Facilities:	NRA licence
Charge:	no
Directions:	turn off A4155 in Medmenham opposite the Dog and Badger Inn
Link:	Oxford Canal, Kennet and Avon, River Wey, Grand Union Canal

Riverside Picnic Grounds, Hurley Farm Ltd, Hurley, Berks

Suits:	craft up to 20' LOA approx
Availability:	0800 to dusk, mar 1st to oct 31st
Restrictions:	none

Facilities:	fuel, parking for car and trailer(c), toilets, telephone: chandlery and boatyard from Peter Freebody and Co, Mill Lane, Hurley
Licence:	NRA licence
Charge:	yes
Directions:	leave M4 at junction 8/9 taking A423 (M) towards Henley-on-Thames, reaching Hurley village after five miles: go through village and turn right after half a mile into Shepherds Lane: the entrance to the Caravan Park is 200yds on left
Link:	Oxford Canal, Kennet and Avon, River Wey, Grand Union Canal

District 3: Temple to Bell Weir-Navigation
Inspector (0628) 22491

Marlow Marine, Harleyford Marina, Marlow, Bucks

Tel: (0628) 471368

Suits:	larger craft up to 10 tons
Availability:	by prior arrangement only
Restrictions:	launching by boat lift only: no slipway
Facilities:	diesel, sewage and refuse disposal, gas, toilets and showers, overnight moorings, chandlery, engine repairs
Licence:	NRA licence
Charge:	yes
Directions:	leave M4 at junction 4 taking A404 and A4155: site is on north bank
Link:	Oxford Canal, Kennet and Avon, River Wey, Grand Union Canal

St. Peter's Street, Marlow, Bucks

Suits:	dinghies and small cabin cruisers
Availability:	during daylight hours
Restrictions:	none
Facilities:	from Harleyford Marina
Licence:	NRA licence
Charge:	no
Directions:	turn off A4155 into High Street in Marlow: turn left at end of street into Station Road, then right into St. Peter's Street
Link:	Oxford Canal, Kennet and Avon, River Wey, Grand Union Canal

Ferry Inn, Cookham, Berks

Suits:	small craft
Availability:	during daylight hours
Restrictions:	none
Facilities:	fuel, parking for car and trailer, telephone, toilets, pub
Charge:	no
Directions:	follow A4094 to Cookham turning into Odney Lane opposite the High Street and then turning left immediately
Link:	Oxford Canal, Kennet and Avon, River Wey, Grand Union Canal

Suits:	small craft
Availability:	during daylight hours
Restrictions:	none
Facilities:	none
Licence:	NRA licence
Charge:	no
Directions:	turn off B3028 into Ferry Road: launch from disused ferry slipway adjacent to Waterside Inn
Link:	Oxford Canal, Kennet and Avon, River Wey, Grand Union Canal

Thames Marine, Bray Marina, Monkey Island Lane, Bray, Berks
Tel: (0628) 773472

Suits:	large craft up to 8 tons
Availability:	0900-1700 mon-fri by prior arrangement only
Restrictions:	no slipway: launching by crane only
Facilities:	fuel, parking for car and trailer(c), sewage and refuse disposal, water, gas, toilets and showers, overnight moorings
Licence:	NRA licence
Charge:	yes
Directions:	leave M4 at junction 9 taking A308 towards Windsor
Link:	Oxford Canal, Kennet and Avon, River Wey, Grand Union Canal

Windsor Marina, Maidenhead Road, Windsor, Berks
Tel: (0753) 853911

Suits:	craft up to 20' LOA
Availability:	0830-1730 daily
Restrictions:	none
Facilities:	fuel, parking for car and trailer(c), sewage and refuse disposal, water, gas, pump-out, toilets and showers, moorings, chandlery and boat-yard with crane, engine repairs
Licence:	NRA licence
Charge:	yes
Directions:	leave M4 at junction 9 taking A308 towards Windsor
Link:	Oxford Canal, Kennet and Avon, River Wey, Grand Union Canal

District 4: Penton Hook to Teddington
Navigation Inspector (0932) 781946

Penton Hook Marina, Staines Road, Chertsey, Surrey
Tel: (0932) 568681

Suits:	craft up to 20' LOA
Availability:	0900-1700 mon-fri, 0900-1600 sat and sun
Restrictions:	steep slipway
Facilities:	fuel, parking for car and trailer(c), telephone, sewage and refuse disposal, water, gas, pump-out, toilets and showers, moorings, chan-

dlery and boatyard with crane, engine repairs

Licence:	NRA licence
Charge:	yes
Directions:	follow signs on A320 to Thorpe Park and marina is opposite
Link:	Oxford Canal, Kennet and Avon, River Wey, Grand Union Canal

Laleham, Surrey

Suits:	all craft
Availability:	during daylight hours
Restrictions:	none
Facilities:	none
Licence:	NRA licence
Charge:	no
Directions:	take B376 Shepperton Road from Staines towards Laleham turning down to river by Three Horseshoes pub
Link:	Oxford Canal, Kennet and Avon, River Wey, Grand Union Canal

Chertsey Meads Marine, The Meads, Chertsey, Surrey
Tel: (0932) 564699

Suits:	craft up to 22' LOA
Availability:	0900-1800 daily
Restrictions:	none
Facilities:	diesel on site, petrol .25 mile, parking for car and trailer(c), refuse disposal, water, gas, toilets, limited chandlery, boatyard
Licence:	NRA licence
Charge:	yes
Directions:	leave M25 at junction 11 and head for Chertsey, following dual carriageway to roundabout and taking first exit; carry on over traffic lights taking Mead Lane, third road on right; follow for half a mile taking first private road on left and follow to end
Link:	Oxford Canal, Kennet and Avon, River Wey, Grand Union Canal

Thames Street, Weybridge, Surrey

Suits:	small craft
Availability:	during daylight hours
Restrictions:	none
Facilities:	available locally
Charge:	no
Directions:	turn off M25 at junction 11 taking A317 to Weybridge: site is adjacent to Weybridge Marine at the junction of Walton Lane and Thames Street
Link:	Oxford Canal, Kennet and Avon, River Wey, Grand Union Canal

Nauticalia, Ferry Lane, Shepperton, Surrey
Tel: (0932) 254844

Suits:	craft up to 42' LOA
Availability:	during working hours

Restrictions:	none
Facilities:	parking for car and trailer(c), at Shepperton Lock, water, toilets, limited chandlery and boatyard
Licence:	NRA licence
Charge:	yes
Directions:	from A3 take A244 to Walton-on-Thames crossing Walton Bridge and turning left onto the B375
Link:	Oxford Canal, Kennet and Avon, River Wey, Grand Union Canal

Shepperton Village Wharf, Surrey

Suits:	all craft
Availability:	during daylight hours
Restrictions:	none
Facilities:	available locally
Licence:	NRA licence
Directions:	follow B375 to Shepperton: site is at end of road by Anchor Inn
Link:	Oxford Canal, Kennet and Avon, River Wey, Grand Union Canal

Gibbs Marine Sales, Sandhills, Russell Road, Shepperton, Surrey
Tel: (0932) 220926

Suits:	craft up to 25′ LOA
Availability:	during working hours by appointment only
Facilities:	fuel, parking for car and trailer, chandlery, toilets, engine repairs
Licence:	NRA licence
Charge:	yes
Directions:	leave the M25 at junction 11 taking the A317 and A244 across the bridge: site is in Russell road opposite the Ship pub
Link:	Oxford Canal, Kennet and Avon, River Wey, Grand Union Canal

Bridge Marine, Thames Meadow, Shepperton, Middx
Tel: (0932) 245126

Suits:	craft up to 24′ LOA on appropriate trailer
Availability:	1000-1700 daily: closed over Christmas
Restrictions:	only 6 DIY launches per day permitted
Facilities:	petrol nearby, parking for car only, toilets, overnight moorings, chandlery and boatyard with 10 ton boat hoist
Licence:	NRA licence
Directions:	leave M25 at junction 11 taking the A317 and A244 across the bridge and turn left and left again into Walton Lane and then into Thames Meadow
Link:	Oxford Canal, Kennet and Avon, River Wey, Grand Union Canal

Marlow Marine Services, Shepperton Marina, Felix Lane, Shepperton, Surrey
Tel: (0932) 247427

Suits:	craft up to 15 tons
Availability:	by prior arrangement
Restrictions:	no slipway: launching by crane only

Facilities:	refuse and sewage disposal, water, gas, toilets and showers, chandlery and boatyard
Licence:	NRA licence
Charge:	yes
Directions:	turn off M25 at junction 11 taking A317 to Walton-on-Thames then follow A244 over bridge: site is downstream of bridge on north bank
Link:	Oxford Canal, Kennet and Avon, River Wey, Grand Union Canal

Cowey Sale, Walton-on-Thames, Surrey

Suits:	small craft
Availability:	during working hours
Restrictions:	none
Facilities:	available locally
Licence:	NRA licence
Charge:	no
Directions:	turn off M25 at junction 11 taking A317 to Walton-on-Thames: site is on south bank upriver of Walton Bridge
Link:	Oxford Canal, Kennet and Avon, River Wey, Grand Union Canal

Walton Wharf, By Anglers Hotel, Walton-on-Thames, Surrey

Suits:	small craft
Availability:	during daylight hours
Restrictions:	none
Facilities:	available locally: pub adjacent
Licence:	NRA licence
Charge:	no
Directions:	site is adjacent to Anglers Hotel in Manor Road, Walton-on-Thames
Link:	Oxford Canal, Kennet and Avon, River Wey, Grand Union Canal

Lower Hampton Road, Sunbury, Surrey

Suits:	small craft
Availability:	during working hours
Restrictions:	none
Facilities:	available locally
Licence:	NRA licence
Charge:	no
Directions:	follow B375 west from Hampton: site is just upriver of Sunbury Court opposite Sunbury Court Island
Link:	Oxford Canal, Kennet and Avon, River Wey, Grand Union Canal

Hurst Park, West Molesey, Surrey

Suits:	all craft
Availability:	during daylight hours
Restrictions:	none
Facilities:	available locally
Licence:	NRA licence
Charge:	no

Directions:	follow Hurst Road (A3050) west from Hampton Court Bridge turning off into Sadlers Ride: site is opposite Garrick's Ait
Link:	Oxford Canal, Kennet and Avon, River Wey, Grand Union Canal

Thames Ditton, Surrey

Suits:	all craft
Availability:	during daylight hours
Restrictions:	none
Facilities:	available locally: pub adjacent
Licence:	NRA licence
Charge:	no
Directions:	turn off A309 into Summer Road: site is next to Swan Hotel and opposite Thames Ditton Island
Link:	Oxford Canal, Kennet and Avon, River Wey, Grand Union Canal

Ditton Reach, Thames Ditton, Surrey

Suits:	all craft
Availability:	during daylight hours
Restrictions:	none
Facilities:	available locally
Licence:	NRA licence
Charge:	no
Directions:	turn off A307
Link:	Oxford Canal, Kennet and Avon, River Wey, Grand Union Canal

Thameside, Kingston-upon-Thames, Surrey

Suits:	all craft
Availability:	during daylight hours
Restrictions:	tidal site: no launching at LW
Facilities:	available from Turks Boatyard adjacent
Licence:	NRA licence
Charge:	yes
Directions:	follow A308 to Kingston Bridge: launch from east bank downriver of bridge and adjacent to Turks Boatyard
Link:	Oxford Canal, Kennet and Avon, River Wey, Grand Union Canal

BELOW TEDDINGTON LOCK (TIDAL RIVER) PORT OF LONDON AUTHORITY

Europe House, World Trade Centre, London E1 9AA
Tel: 071-481 8484

Pleasure craft should keep clear of commercial vessels and beware strong currents which may carry them into moored barges. Speed should be limited to prevent excess wash: above Wandsworth Bridge there is a speed limit of 8 knots. It is strongly recommended that before launching at any of the sites listed below, visitors should contact the Harbour Master (see below) for the latest information regarding navigation on the river and availability of sites which may sometimes be obstructed by commercial craft.

Upper Section (Twickenham-Woolwich) 071-265 2656

Teddington Draw Dock, Teddington, Middx.

081-940 8723

Suits:	craft up to 15' LOA
Availability:	launching into 6' water at HWS: 2' drop at end of slipway at LW
Restrictions:	get key to locked gate from Tough Bros, Teddington Wharf Tel: 081-9777 4494
Facilities:	fuel (2 miles), limited parking for car only, refuse disposal and water at lock, chandlery from Suntest, Ferry Road, boatyard at Tough Bros
Licence:	none
Charge:	no
Directions:	site is at end of Ferry Road just downriver of lock
Link:	Grand Union Canal, Oxford Canal, River Wey, North Sea

Church Lane, Twickenham, Middx

Suits:	small craft only
Availability:	tidal site: no launching at LW
Restrictions:	narrow access: launching over hard gravel foreshore
Licence:	none
Charge:	no
Directions:	turn off A305 in Twickenham into Church Lane and follow to Embankment
Link:	Grand Union Canal, Oxford Canal, River Wey, North Sea

Riverside, Twickenham, Middx

Suits:	small craft only
Availability:	tidal site: no launching at LW
Restrictions:	narrow access
Facilities:	available locally, pub nearby
Licence:	none
Charge:	no
Directions:	follow the A305 into Twickenham: site is opposite White Swan Inn
Link:	Grand Union Canal, Oxford Canal, River Wey, North Sea

Ham Landing, Ham, Surrey

Suits:	small craft
Availability:	tidal site: no launching at LW
Restrictions:	popular site which can be congested
Facilities:	parking in adjacent car park
Licence:	none
Charge:	no
Directions:	turn off A307 following lane to Ham Landing
Link:	Grand Union Canal, Oxford Canal, River Wey, North Sea

River Lane, Petersham, Surrey

Suits:	small craft
Availability:	tidal site: best launching near HW
Restrictions:	site may be congested
Facilities:	none
Charge:	no
Directions:	turn off A307 on sharp bend into River Lane
Link:	Grand Union Canal, Oxford Canal, River Wey, North Sea

Drawdock, Water Lane, Richmond, Surrey

Suits:	small craft
Availability:	tidal site: best launching near HW
Restrictions:	site is often congested and access is narrow
Facilities:	available locally
Licence:	none
Charge:	no
Directions:	follow A307/A305: site is just downriver of Richmond Bridge
Link:	Grand Union Canal, Oxford Canal, River Wey, North Sea

London Apprentice Inn, Church Street, Isleworth, London

Suits:	craft up to 40' LOA and 10' wide
Availability:	tidal site: best launching for approximately 2 hours either side of HW
Restrictions:	none
Facilities:	fuel, parking for car and trailer, toilets, telephone
Licence:	none
Charge:	no
Directions:	turn off A315 into Park Road and then into Church Street
Link:	Grand Union Canal, Oxford Canal, River Wey, North Sea

Drawdock, Kew Bridge, London

Suits:	small craft
Availability:	tidal site: launch near HW
Restrictions:	site is very muddy at LW
Facilities:	none
Licence:	none
Charge:	no

Directions: site is adjacent to and downstream of bridge on north bank of river
Link: Grand Union Canal, Oxford Canal, River Wey, North Sea

Grove Park Drawdock, Kew, London

Suits: small craft
Availability: tidal site: launch near HW
Restrictions: congested access
Facilities: none
Licence: none
Charge: no
Directions: site is at end of Grove Park Road immediately downriver of Kew railway bridge
Link: Grand Union Canal, Oxford Canal, River Wey, North Sea

Ship Drawdock, Mortlake, London

Suits: small craft
Availability: tidal site: launch near HW
Restrictions: park well above tidal limit, road may flood at HW
Facilities: parking close by
Licence: none
Charge: no
Directions: turn off Lower Richmond Road into Ship Lane
Link: Grand Union Canal, Oxford Canal, River Wey, North Sea

Small Profits Drawdock, Barnes, London

Suits: small craft
Availability: best launching near HW
Restrictions: access may be congested
Facilities: none
Licence: none
Charge: no
Directions: turn off Lonsdale Road
Link: Grand Union Canal, Oxford Canal, River Wey, North Sea

Chiswick Church Drawdock, Church Street, Chiswick, London

Suits: small craft
Availability: tidal site: launch near HW
Restrictions: access may be congested
Facilities: none
Licence: none
Charge: no
Directions: site is at end of Church Street, Chiswick
Link: Grand Union Canal, Oxford Canal, River Wey, North Sea

Hammersmith Drawdock, Hammersmith, London

Suits:	small craft
Availability:	tidal site: launch near HW
Restrictions:	access may be congested
Facilities:	none
Licence:	none
Charge:	no
Directions:	site is downriver of Hammersmith Bridge
Link:	Grand Union Canal, Oxford Canal, River Wey, North Sea

Putney Drawdock, Putney, London

Suits:	small craft
Availability:	tidal site: best launching near HW
Restrictions:	access may be congested
Facilities:	none
Licence:	none
Charge:	no
Directions:	site is immediately upriver of Putney Bridge on the Embankment
Link:	Grand Union Canal, Oxford Canal, River Wey, North

Brewhouse Street, Putney, London

Suits:	small craft
Availability:	tidal site: launch near HW
Restrictions:	access may be congested
Facilities:	none
Licence:	none
Charge:	yes
Directions:	site is downriver of Putney Bridge: turn off Putney Road
Link:	Grand Union Canal, Oxford Canal, River Wey, North Sea

Battersea Drawdock, Battersea, London

Suits:	small craft
Availability:	tidal site: launch near HW
Restrictions:	access may be congested
Facilities:	none
Licence:	none
Charge:	no
Directions:	site is near Church and access is from Battersea Church Road
Link:	Grand Union Canal, Oxford Canal, River Wey, North Sea

Newcastle Drawdock and Johnsons Drawdock, Isle of Dogs, London

Suits:	small craft
Availability:	tidal site: launch near HW
Restrictions:	site may be congested
Facilities:	none
Licence:	none

Charge: no
Directions: access is from Saunders Ness Road
Link: Grand Union Canal, Oxford Canal, River Wey, North Sea

Samuda Housing Estate, Isle of Dogs, London

Suits: small craft
Availability: tidal site: launch within 3 hours HW
Restrictions: none
Facilities: parking for car and trailer nearby
Licence: none
Charge: no
Directions: access is from Manchester Road
Link: Grand Union Canal, Oxford Canal, River Wey, North Sea

Point Drawdock, Greenwich, London

Suits: small craft
Availability: tidal site: launch near HW
Restrictions: access may be congested
Facilities: none
Charge: no
Directions: turn off Tunnel Avenue into Drawdock Road
Link: Grand Union Canal, Oxford Canal, River Wey, North Sea

Bugsby's Hole Causeway, Greenwich, London

Suits: small craft
Availability: tidal site: launch near HW
Restrictions: access may be congested
Facilities: none
Licence: none
Charge: no
Directions: fork off Tunnel Avenue (which leads to the Blackwall Tunnel) into
               Blackwall Lane, turning off to causeway: site is at end of River Way
Link: Grand Union Canal, Oxford Canal, River Wey, North Sea

Lower Section (Woolwich – Sea Reach) (0474) 562200

Barge House Road, Woolwich, London

Suits: small craft
Availability: tidal site: concrete slipway but site is muddy at LW
Restrictions: access may be congested
Facilities: none
Licence: none
Charge: no
Directions: turn off Woolwich Manor Way/Albert Road
Link: Grand Union Canal, Oxford Canal, River Wey, North Sea

Bell Water Gate, Woolwich, London

Suits: small craft
Availability: tidal site: launch near HW
Restrictions: steep ramp
Facilities: parking is difficult
Licence: none
Charge: no
Directions: access is from Woolwich High Street
Link: Grand Union Canal, Oxford Canal, River Wey, North Sea

Gravesend Canal Basin, Gravesend, Kent
Tel: (0474) 352392/337489

Suits: all craft
Availability: at all states of tide
Restrictions: lock opens from one hour before to HW
Facilities: petrol, parking for car and trailer in compound(c), toilets and showers, chandlers nearby, crane
Licence: licence required
Charge: yes
Directions: turn off M2 following signs to Gravesend East, going along Valley Drive and into Abbey Road, turning left into Milton Road and then right into Ordnance Road: turn left at Canal Road onto the Promenade and look for the wooden bridge: site is adjacent
Link: Grand Union Canal, Oxford Canal, River Wey, North Sea

RIVER TRENT   BW (North East Region)

Richard Mercer, 24 Meadow Lane, Nottingham NG2 3HL
Tel: (0602) 862411

The river runs for almost 100 miles from the Midlands to the Humber Estuary, giving access to the Sheffield and South Yorkshire Navigation, the Chesterfield Canal, the Fossdyke and Witham Navigation, the Erewash Canal, the River Soar Navigation and the Trent and Mersey Canal. Below Cromwell Lock the river is tidal. There is a speed limit of 8mph downstream of Long Eaton and 6mph upstream. Water-skiing is allowed in some areas.

Sawley Marina, Trent Lock, Long Eaton, Nottingham, Notts
Tel: (0602) 734278

Suits: all craft
Availability: 0830-1800 daily
Restrictions: none
Facilities: fuel, parking for car and trailer(c), sewage and refuse disposal, water, gas, pump-out, toilets and showers, overnight moorings, chandlery, boatyard with crane, restaurant
Licence: BW licence
Charge: yes

76

Directions: leave M1 at junction 24 taking A6 towards Derby then turn right to
                  Long Eaton on B6540
Link: see paragraph above

Beeston Marina, Riverside Road, Beeston,Rylands, Nottingham, Notts
Tel: (0602) 223168

Suits: all craft
Availability: 0800-1800 daily
Restrictions: none
Facilities: fuel, no parking, water, gas,. toilets and showers, overnight moor-
                  ings, chandlery, boatyard with crane, coffee shop
Licence: BW licence
Charge: yes
Directions: Follow signs from Queens Road/Station Road in Beeston to the marina
Link: see paragraph above

Nottingham Castle Marina, Castle Boulevard, Nottingham, Notts
Tel: (0602) 412672

Suits: all craft
Availability: 0900-1700 on weekdays only: no launching at weekends
Restrictions: none
Facilities: diesel, sewage and refuse disposal, water, gas, pump-out, toilets,
                  overnight moorings, chandlery
Licence: BW licence
Charge: yes
Directions: leave M1 at junction 25 taking A52 to city
Link: see paragraph above

Ferry Boat Inn, Stoke Bardolph, Nottingham, Notts

Suits: all craft
Availability: 0900-2100 daily
Restrictions: none
Facilities: fuel, parking for car(c), toilets, telephone, pub adjacent
Licence: BW licence
Charge: yes
Directions: take A612 north east from Nottingham and turn off following signs to
                  the village
Link: see paragraph above

Star and Garter Public House, Hazelford Ferry, Bleasby, Nottingham, Notts

Suits: all craft
Availability: during daylight hours
Facilities: fuel (3 miles), parking for car and trailer(c), toilets, telephone, pub
Licence: BW licence
Charge: no
Directions: take the A612 north-east from Nottingham to Thurgarton: turn right
                  at the Coach and Horses and follow signs to Bleasby
Link: see paragraph above

Farndon Harbour, Farndon, Nr. Newark, Notts

Tel: (0636) 705483

Suits: all craft
Availability: launch during working hours
Restrictions: none
Facilitites: diesel on site, petrol (1 mile), parking for car and trailer(c), sewage
               and refuse disposal, water, gas, toilets and showers, overnight moor-
               ings, limited chandlery, boatyard with crane and boat hoist, engine
               repairs
Licence: BW licence
Charge: yes
Directions: follow A46 south from Newark turning into Farndon main street then
               right into Marsh Lane, left into Nursery Avenue and right to harbour
Link: see paragraph above

TRENT AND MERSEY CANAL BW (Midlands and North West Region)

Trentham to Derwentmouth
Stephen Goode, Fradley Junction, Alrewas, Burton-on-Trent, Staffordshire DE13
7DN Tel: (0283) 790236

Preston Brook to Trentham
Peter Bentham, Lighterage Yard, Chesterway, Northwich, Cheshire CW9 5JT
Tel: (0606) 40566

The canal runs for 93 miles from Derwentmouth to Preston Brook and has junctions
with a number of other canals. It was an extremely successful waterway, carrying
china clay and flint for the potteries and taking away finished goods. There is a speed
limit of 4mph.

Sawley Marina, Trent Lock, Long Eaton, Nottingham, Notts

Tel: (0602) 734278

Suits: all craft
Availability: 0830-1800 daily
Restrictions: none
Facilitites: fuel, parking for car and trailer(c), sewage and refuse disposal, water,
               gas,pump-out, toilets and showers, overnight moorings, chandlery
               boatyard with crane, restaurant
Licence: BW licence
Charge: yes
Directions: leave M1 at junction 24 taking A6 towards Derby, then turn right to
               Long Eaton on B6540
Link: River Trent, Erewash Canal, River Soar Navigation, Coventry Canal,
               Staffs and Worcs Canal, Caldon Canal, Macclesfield Canal

Dobsons of Shardlow Ltd. The Wharf, Shardlow, Derby
Tel: (0332) 792271

Suits:	craft up to 25' LOA with suitable draught
Availability:	0900-1730 mon-fri, 0900-1700 sat, 1000-1600 sun
Restrictions:	none
Facilities:	diesel, petrol nearby, parking for car and trailer(c), sewage and refuse disposal, water, gas, pump-out, toilets, overnight moorings, chandlery and boatyard
Licence:	BW licence
Charge:	yes
Directions:	leave M1 at junction 24 taking the A6 towards Derby, turning off to follow signs to Shardlow
Link:	River Trent, Erewash Canal, River Soar Navigation, Coventry Canal, Staffs and Worcs Canal, Caldon Canal, Macclesfield Canal

Midland Canal Centre, Stenson Marina, Stenson, Derbys
Tel: (0283) 701933

Suits:	all craft
Availability:	during working hours by prior arrangement only
Restrictions:	none
Facilities:	diesel, petrol nearby, parking for car and trailer(c), sewage disposal, water, gas, pump-out, toilets, overnight moorings, chandlery and boatyard
Licence:	BW licence
Charge:	yes
Directions:	follow the A38 south from Derby taking the A5132 east to Twyford, then follow minor roads
Link:	River Trent, Erewash Canal, River Soar Navigation, Coventry Canal, Staffs and Worcs Canal, Caldon Canal, Macclesfield Canal

Jannel Cruisers Ltd, Shobnall Marina, Shobnall Road, Burton-on-Trent, Derbys
Tel: (0283) 42718

Suits:	all craft
Availability:	0900-1700 but advance notice required
Restrictions:	by prior arrangement only
Facilities:	diesel, petrol nearby, parking for car and trailer(c), sewage and refuse disposal, water, gas, pump-out, toilets, overnight moorings, boatyard
Licence:	BW licence
Charge:	yes
Directions:	leave the A38 at south Burton turn off signposted A5121 Burton: turn left onto B5234 for two miles and turn left at traffic island: the site is then 200yds along Shobnall Road on the left hand side
Link:	River Trent, Erewash Canal, River Soar Navigation, Coventry Canal, Staffs and Worcs Canal, Caldon Canal, Macclesfield Canal

The Stone Boatbuilding Co Ltd, Newcastle Road, Stone, Staffs
Tel: (0785) 812688

Suits:	narrow boats and cruisers
Availability:	0900-1730 mon-fri
Restrictions:	none
Facilities:	diesel, petrol (.5 mile), parking for car and trailer(c) by arrangement only, sewage and refuse disposal, water, gas, pump-out, toilets and showers, chandlery, boatyard, engine repairs
Licence:	BW licence
Charge:	yes
Directions:	follow the A34 south turning off into Stone and onto B5027
Link:	River Trent, Erewash Canal, River Soar Navigation, Coventry Canal, Staffs and Worcs Canal, Caldon Canal, Macclesfield Canal

Dolphin Boats, Old Whieldon Road, Stoke-on-Trent, Staffs
Tel: (0782) 49390

Suits:	all craft up to 30' LOA
Availability:	during daylight hours
Restrictions:	none
Facilities:	petrol, parking for car and trailer(c), water , gas, overnight moorings, chandlery, boatyard, engine repairs
Licence:	BW licence
Charge:	yes
Directions:	turn off M6 onto the A500: site is by bridge 112
Link:	River Trent, Erewash Canal, River Soar Navigation, Coventry Canal, Staffs and Worcs Canal, Caldon Canal, Macclesfield Canal

Stoke-on-Trent Boatbuilding, Longport Wharf, Longport, Stoke-on-Trent, Staffs
Tel: (0782) 813831

Suits:	all craft
Availability:	0900-1700 daily
Restrictions:	steep slipway
Facilities:	diesel, parking for car and trailer(c), sewage and refuse disposal, water, gas, pump-out, toilets, overnight moorings, chandlery, boatyard, engine repairs
Licence:	BW licence
Charge:	yes
Directions:	leave the M6 at junction 15/16 taking the A500,A527 and B5051
Link:	River Trent, Erewash Canal, River Soar Navigation, Coventry Canal, Staffs and Worcs Canal, Caldon Canal, Macclesfield Canal

RIVER TYNE   Port of Tyne Authority
Tel: 091-257 0407

This is a busy commercial river: all boats are subject to a minimum conservancy charge by the Port of Tyne Authority. There is a speed limit of 6 mph on the river and all waterborne activities are subject to the Authority's bylaws.

Hebburn Marina, Prince Consort Road, Hebburn, Tyne and Wear
Tel: 091-427 1717 (South Tyneside Council) or

Suits:	small craft
Availability:	best launching near HW: site is used by Hebburn Marina Boat Club
Restrictions:	cobbled slipway
Facilities:	parking for car and trailer
Licence:	Port of Tyne Authority
Charge:	no
Directions:	from Hebburn railway station, cross line on flyover following road to roundabout: turn left and go down steep road to river
Link:	North Sea

Lower Walker, Riverside Park, Newcastle-upon-Tyne, Tyne and Wear
Tel: 091-295 0260 (Edwina Simmons)

Suits:	dinghies and trailer-sailers
Availability:	for approximately 2 hours either side HW
Restrictions:	fairly steep slipway: collect key from Vic Burns at Walker Wheels
Facilities:	fuel (1 mile), parking for car and trailer (not overnight), toilets
Licence:	Port of Tyne Authority
Charge:	no
Directions:	take A186 Walker Road to Walker Pottery Bank and Riverside Park: access is via a steep, winding road from Pottery Bank car park
Link:	North Sea

Friar's Goose Water Sports Club, Riverside Park, Green Lane, Gateshead
Tel: 091-469 2549

Suits:	all trailable craft
Availability:	launching for 2/3 hours either side HW
Restrictions:	none
Facilities:	fuel from local garage, parking for car and trailer, toilets and showers at clubhouse, overnight moorings, travel lift
Licence:	Port of Tyne Authority
Charge:	yes
Directions:	follow A6127 from the A1(M) into Gateshead: site is on south bank
Link:	North Sea

Derwenthaugh Marina, Gateshead, Tyne and Wear
Tel: 091-499 0133

Suits:	craft up to 35' LOA
Availability:	launching for approximately 5 hours either side HW
Restrictions:	all craft launching must have third party insurance
Facilities:	fuel, parking for car and trailer, toilets and telephone, chandlers
Licence:	Port of Tyne Authority
Charge:	yes
Directions:	follow signs from the A69: site is on south bank of river at the confluence of the rivers Tyne and Derwent near Blaydon
Link:	North Sea

Tel: 091-264 0014 (Newburn Riverside Recreation Assoc).

Suits:	small craft only
Availability:	for approximately 2 hours either side HW
Restrictions:	launching by prior arrangement only
Facilities:	fuel, (.5 mile), parking for car and trailer, (not overnight), toilets
Licence:	Port of Tyne Authority
Charge:	yes
Directions:	take A6085 Newcastle to Newburn road, turning off in Newburn
Link:	North Sea

UNION CANAL   BW (Scotland Region)

Jim Nelson, Rosebank House, Main Street, Camelon, Falkirk FK1 4DS
Tel: (0324) 612415

Built in the 19th century to supply building materials to Edinburgh and originally
connected to the Forth and Clyde Canal at Falkirk by a flight of 11 locks, the canal is
now obstructed by road crossings but has reasonable cruising lengths. There is a
speed limit of 3mph on the canal.

Manse Road Basin, Manse Road, Linlithgow, Lothian

Suits:	craft up to 13' LOA and 7' wide
Availability:	during daylight hours
Restrictions:	site is regularly used by local canal society
Facilities:	fuel, parking for car and trailer by arrangement, toilets
Licence:	BW licence
Charge:	no
Directions:	follow the B9080 west from Edinburgh; site is near railway station
Link:	navigable to Broxburn (8 miles)

East Church Street, Broxburn, Nr. Linlithgow, Lothian

Suits:	craft up to 25' LOA
Availability:	during daylight hours
Restrictions:	key to gate from BW or Sports Centre, East Main Street Broxburn, Tel: (0506) 854997
Facilities:	fuel, parking for cars, toilets and telephone
Licence:	BW licence
Charge:	no
Directions:	follow the A8, A89/899 west from Edinburgh: access is off East Main Road and the site is near Broxburn Sports Centre
Link:	navigable to Linlithgow (8 miles)

Harrison Park, Edinburgh

Suits:	craft up to 13' LOA
Availability:	during daylight hours

Restrictions:	slipway is small wooden ramp: this area is regularly used by rowers
Facilities:	fuel, parking for cars, toilets and telephone
Licence:	BW licence
Charge:	no
Directions:	turn off A70 Slateford Road into Harrison Road then into Harrison Gardens: site is on corner of Ashley Drive and Ogilvy Terrace
Link:	navigable to Slateford Aqueduct

Greenbank Road Slipway, Falkirk, Central

Suits:	small craft up to 8' wide
Availability:	during daylight hours
Restrictions:	steep slipway of loose stone
Facilities:	none
Licence:	BW licence
Charge:	no
Directions:	turn off A803 west out of Falkirk into Glenfluir Road then into Greenbank Road car park
Link:	navigable for 1.5 miles

RIVER WEAR   Port of Sunderland
Tel: 091-514 0411 (Harbour Master)

This is a busy commercial river with a speed limit of 6 knots. Access to the sea from the upper reaches is limited to 3 hours either side HW by a barrier.

Sir James Steel Park, Nr. Washington, Tyne and Wear

Suits:	craft up to 20' LOA
Availability:	2 hours either side HW
Restrictions:	tidal site ten miles from river mouth
Facilities:	parking for car and trailer, toilets
Licence:	harbour dues payable
Charge:	yes
Directions:	turn off A1(M) south of the Washington Services: site is on north bank
Link:	North Sea

Fatfield, Nr. Washington, Tyne and Wear

Suits:	craft up to 20' LOA
Availability:	2.5 hours either side HW
Restrictions:	tidal site nine miles from river mouth
Facilities:	parking for car and trailer
Licence:	harbour dues payable
Charge:	yes
Directions:	turn off A1 (M) south of the Washington Services
Link:	North Sea

Suits:	craft up to 20' LOA
Availability:	3 hours either side HW
Restrictions:	tidal site and steep slipway
Facilities:	fuel from nearby garage, parking for car and trailer, pub adjacent
Licence:	harbour dues payable
Charge:	yes
Directions:	leave A1 (M) taking A183 east and turning off to South Hylton: site is five miles from mouth and adjacent to Golden Lion pub
Link:	North Sea

Claxhaugh, Sunderland, Tyne and Wear

Suits:	craft up to 20' LOA
Availability:	3 hours either side HW
Restrictions:	tidal site four miles from river mouth
Facilities:	parking for car and trailer
Licence:	harbour dues payable
Charge:	yes
Directions:	follow A690 from A1 (M) to Sunderland: site is on south bank
Link:	North Sea

RIVER WEY AND GODALMING NAVIGATION   (National Trust)

Dapdune Wharf, Wharf Road, Guildford GU1 4RR
Tel: (0483) 61389

The river joins the Thames below Shepperton Lock and is owned by the National Trust. It is navigable for nearly 20 miles to Godalming and gives access to the Basingstoke Canal at Woodham Junction. There is a speed limit of 4 knots and engine size is restricted to 1 HP per foot length up to a max size of 20 HP.

Pyrford Marina, Lock Lane, Pyrford, Woking, Surrey
Tel: (0392) 340739

Suits:	craft up to 25/30' LOA with appropriate engine size
Availability:	during daylight hours
Restrictions:	do not approach via Ripley Road: there is a narrow bridge
Facilities:	diesel, petrol (1 mile), parking for car and trailer(c), sewage and refuse disposal, water, gas, pump-out, toilets and showers, boatyard
Licence:	National Trust
Charge:	yes
Directions:	leave A3 at Cobham roundabout, taking A245 to West Byfleet and turning off down Pyrford Road then into Lock Lane
Link:	River Thames, Basingstoke Canal

Stoke Lock, Guildford, Surrey
Tel: (0483) 504939

Suits:	craft up to 25' LOA with appropriate engine size
Availability:	daylight hours by arrangement
Restrictions:	none
Facilities:	fuel, parking for car and trailer(c), telephone
Licence:	National Trust
Charge:	yes
Directions:	turn off the A320 Woking road into Moorfield Road: site is behind the Slyfield Industrial Estate
Link:	River Thames, Basingstoke Canal

RIVER WITHAM (WITHAM AND FOSSDYKE NAVIGATION)
BW (North East Region)

Richard Mercer, 24 Meadow Lane, Nottingham NG2 3HL
Tel: (0602) 862411

The Fossdyke Navigation is the oldest artificially constructed waterway in the country and was designed to connect the River Witham to the Trent and Humber. There is a speed limit of 3mph.

Brayford Wharf East, Brayford Pool, Lincoln, Lincs

Suits:	craft up to 18' LOA
Availability:	during daylight hours
Restrictions:	steep slipway
Facilities:	fuel, parking for cars only, toilets, chandlery and boatyard nearby
Licence:	no
Charge:	no
Directions:	from City centre, take Wigford Way to Brayford Pool
Link:	Witham Navigable Drains, River Trent, Humber Estuary

James Kendall and Co. Lincoln Marina, Brayford Pool, Lincoln, Lincs
Tel: (0522) 526896

Suits:	all craft
Availability:	0900-1700 daily
Restrictions:	none
Facilities:	diesel, parking for car and trailer(c), refuse disposal, water, gas, toilets, overnight moorings, chandlery and boatyard
Licence:	BW licence
Charge:	yes
Directions:	from City centre, take Wigford Way to Brayford Pool
Link:	Witham Navigable Drains, River Trent, Humber Estuary

Belle Isle Marina, Dogdyke Road, Coningsby, Lincs

Tel: (0526) 42124

Suits:	craft up to 22' LOA
Availability:	during working hours
Restrictions:	none
Facilities:	fuel, parking for car and trailer, sewage and refuse disposal, water, pump-out, toilets and showers, overnight moorings, boatyard
Licence:	BW licence
Charge:	yes
Directions:	from A153 north of Sleaford take Dogdyke Road for two miles
Link:	Witham Navigable Drains, River Trent, Humber Estuary

WORCESTER AND BIRMINGHAM CANAL   BW (Midland Region)

Glynn Phillips, Canal Office, New Wharf, Tardebigge, Bromsgrove, Worcestershire
B60 1NF
Tel: (0527) 72572

Now part of the popular cruising circuit, the canal runs for 30 miles from Diglis in Worcester, where it connects with the River Severn to King's Norton where the Stratford-on-Avon Canal enters and ends in Birmingham.

Alvechurch Boat Centre, Scarfield Wharf, Alvechurch, Hereford and Worcester

Tel: 021-445 2909

Suits:	all craft
Availability:	by prior arrangement only: no casual launching
Restrictions:	none
Facilities:	diesel, parking for car and trailer(c), sewage and refuse disposal, water, gas, pump-out, toilets, chandlery and boatyard
Licence:	BW licence
Charge:	yes
Directions:	follow the A441 to Redditch: turn right in Alvechurch up Bear Lane
Link:	River Severn, Stratford-on-Avon Canal, Birmingham Canal

Saraband Boat Centre, Hanbury Wharf, Droitwich, Hereford and Worcester

Tel: (0905) 771018

Suits:	craft up to 40' LOA and 6'10" wide
Availability:	0900-1800 mon-sat, 1000-1800 sun
Restrictions:	none
Facilities:	diesel, parking for car and trailer(c), toilets, chandlery and boatyard
Licence:	BW licence
Charge:	yes
Directions:	follow A38 to Droitwich town centre then B4090 east for two miles
Link:	River Severn, Stratford-on-Avon Canal, Birmingham Canal

Index